THE BREAK THROUGH THE WALL

WEEK-BY-WEEK WORKOUT TRACKER

THE BREAK THROUGH THE WALL

WEEK-BY-WEEK WORKOUT TRACKER

with motivation and inspiration from world-champion athletes

TO PUSH YOU TO THE **NEXT LEVEL**

METRO BOOKS
New York

METRO BOOKS
New York

An Imprint of Sterling Publishing
1166 Avenue of the Americas
New York, NY 10036

METRO BOOKS and the distinctive Metro Books logo
are trademarks of Sterling Publishing Co., Inc.

Conceived, designed, and produced by
Quid Publishing
Level 4 Sheridan House
114 Western Road
Hove BN3 1DD
England
www.quidpublishing.com

ISBN: 978-1-4351-6222-8

For information about custom editions, special sales, and premium and corporate purchases, please contact Sterling Special Sales at 800-805-5489 or specialsales@sterlingpublishing.com.

The information contained herein is provided for educational purposes only and is not intended to substitute for consultation with a health-care provider. Before starting an exercise program, consult a physician.

The athletes portrayed, discussed, and quoted herein are neither affiliated with, nor are sponsors or endorsers of the Break-Through-the-Wall Week-by-Week Workout Tracker *or any recommendations provided herein.*

Manufactured in China

1 3 5 7 9 10 8 6 4 2

www.sterlingpublishing.com

CONTENTS

Using this *Workout Tracker*

So you've decided to be serious about your workout. There are many reasons for doing so, such as maintaining your physical and mental well-being, as well as longevity and quality of life. But it's not always easy to stay on track. Everyone needs a little extra boost sometimes, and, unless you can afford your own personal trainer, it's up to you to do the motivating. ***The Break Through the Wall Week-by-Week Workout Tracker*** should be your companion on all of your workouts. It has everything that you need to record and monitor your daily workout over a six-month period—and to keep track of all those walls you're going to be breaking through.

You can be your own best personal trainer. But you need that edge that will put you ahead of the rest. This resource for tracking your workouts enables you to keep track of your progress and helps you pay close attention to all the elements that make you the athlete you strive to be—your daily activities, dietary intake, energy levels, successes, setbacks, and overall growth as an athlete. It's designed to follow you through a six-month workout period—long enough to see real progress, but not so long that your goals seem out of reach.

Many athletes have long-term goals, such as completing a marathon or bench-pressing a huge weight. But this training tracker allows you to set a goal for each day, a focus for when your larger objectives may seem very far off. Perhaps the wall you're breaking through today is cycling that extra mile, adding six reps to a weight exercise, or paying extra attention to a particular muscle group. The knowledge—and achievement—of smaller goals will drive you through your workout and make you the athlete with an edge on the rest.

Over time you will learn more about your body and how it reacts to certain changes in your workout, diet, and daily activity. No matter what the skill level, you can develop a program that is right for you, and one that you can stick with. And when your six-month regimen is complete, you'll have a detailed record of how you got there. By recording your resistance training, cardiovascular workouts, nutrition, and other specifics, you'll learn what worked and what didn't, what factors made you stronger or weaker—and what pushed you to break through the wall.

Your *Workout Tracker* is broken down into five components:

1. ***Personal Information***

   This is where you keep your vital stats. These are the body specifics when you began your workout course, such as weight, height, and age. You'll need this to determine your ideal heart rate and body weight using the charts at the back of this book. Your personal information is also a good basis of comparison when looking back after you've completed the six-month regimen.

2. ***Daily Trackers***

   Every day for twenty-six weeks you will monitor your workout. You'll log in the type and amount of resistance training you performed, including specific muscle groups that were worked on, type of exercise, warm-up, how many sets you performed, sustained heart rate, your cooldown, and comments on your performance along the way. In addition to logging your physical activities, you also record your dietary intake, including the day's count of calories, carbohydrates and protein. This daily log assists you in monitoring your nutrition and its influence on your weight and energy levels.

   At the end of the day, in your daily journal, you'll grade your day's performance and write down the day's successes or disappointments. This aids you in staying keyed into your body's progress. Remember, achieving your goal is often as much mental as it is physical. To encourage you along the way, your journal is filled with inspirational words from successful athletes who have achieved their own goals. Twenty-six champion athletes from a range of sports offer their support. Their encouraging words help you stay focused on what's important—your ultimate goal of personal fitness. Each of them has hit a wall at one time or another and succeeded in breaking it down. They know firsthand that giving up is never an option.

3. ***Weekly Journal***
Each week you'll reflect upon your accomplishments. What did you learn? How have your routines changed for the better? How close do you feel to your long-term goals? You can refer to the prior weeks' setbacks and improvements to monitor how you've changed, and to see your goals getting closer, as each week passes.

4. ***Heart Rate Chart***
Learn how to calculate your desired heart rate and learn why it is important to monitor. Charts and basic information are provided.

5. ***Ideal Body Weights***
Learn how to calculate your ideal body weight and find out why this is important in your overall fitness outlook. Charts and basic information are provided.

Get started with your ***Workout Tracker***. Have it at hand for each mile or kilometer you run on the treadmill, each lap you swim, each set you bench-press, and learn to meet—and surpass—your own goals.

PERSONAL INFORMATION

YOUR VITAL STATS

NAME

AGE

HEIGHT

WEIGHT

HEART RATE INFORMATION

Maximal Heart Rate (see page 200)

Target Heart Rate Range (see page 200)

YOUR *BREAK-THROUGH-THE-WALL* GOALS

Long-term Goals

Ideal Body Weight

Workout Program Start Date

Workout Program Finish Date

Comments

SAMPLE ENTRY

Enter the date

Establish a goal for the day

Note the muscle group you're working

Record the name of each exercise

List the type of cardio exercise you're performing

Note the length of your warm-up

Record your sustained heart rate

Note the length of your workout at your sustained heart rate

Note the length of your cooldown

WEEK 11 Inspiration: JACKIE JOYNER-KERSEE

Six-time Olympic medalist at track and field

MONDAY DATE Jan. 12

VITAL STATS: Hometown: East St. Louis, Illinois
Born: March 3, 1962
Height: 5 ft 10 in / 178 cm Weight : 150 lb / 68 kg

GOAL FOR THE DAY
30–40 minutes cardio; full lower-body workout

RESISTANCE TRAINING

Muscle Group	Exercise	Warm-Up	Set 1	Set 2	Set 3	Cooldown	Comments
Inner Thighs	Hip Abductor	30 / 12	60 / 10	70 / 10	80 / 10	40 / 12	Tight
Outer thighs	Hip Abductor	40 / 12	80 / 10	90 / 10	100 / 10	50 / 12	Tiring
Calves	Donkey Calf	80 / 12	120 / 10	130 / 10	140 / 10	100 / 12	Nice Increase
Hamstring/ Quads	Leg Press	50 / 10	70 / 8	80 / 8	80 / 9	60 / 10	Toughest exercise!
Quads	Leg Extension	20 / 12	40 / 10	50 / 10	60 / 10	30 / 12	Bump up next time
Hamstrings	Seated Leg Curl	—	30 / 10	40 / 10	50 / 10	—	A Challenge
Abs	Abs Machine	30 / 12	50 / 10	60 / 10	70 / 10	40 / 12	No problem

CARDIO ACTIVITY

Type of Exercise	Warm-Up Period	Sustained Heart Rate	Workout Period In Sustained Heart Rate	Cooldown Period
Stairmaster	5	155	15	5
Pool	5	145	25	5

DIET

Day's Calories	Carbohydrates	Protein	Weight
2000	1000	300	134

STRENGTH

SUCCESS/DISAPPOINTMENT OF THE DAY
Good weight session, but could have swum harder.

Overall Grade: A | (B) | C | D | F How I felt today: Exhausted | Slow | (Average) | Strong | Unstoppable

Asthma could have sidelined her; instead, it strengthened her resolve. At thirteen, **JACKIE JOYNER** saw the biopic of Babe Didrikson, an early women's champion at an array of sports, and vowed to become an all-around athlete. On a basketball scholarship to UCLA, Jackie met Coach Bob Kersee, whom she later married. Encouraged by him, she blazed through the grueling trials of the heptathlon. Scooping up competitive medals and sportsmanship awards, Jackie has gone the distance and left her mark as the "world's greatest female athlete."

TUESDAY | DATE Jan. 13

GOAL FOR THE DAY

Hard run!

List the amount of weight lifted in pounds or kilograms

Record the number of repetitions performed within each set

Enter any comments, good or bad, about each exercise

RESISTANCE TRAINING

Muscle Group	Exercise	Warm-Up	Set 1	Set 2	Set 3	Cooldown	Comments
Upper Back	Lat Pulldown	30 / 12	50 / 10	50 / 10	60 / 10	40 / 12	Easy
Deltoids, Triceps	Overhead Press	—	20 / 10	20 / 10	30 / 10	—	Tough!
Chest	Vertical chest Press	stretch	30 / 10	30 / 10	30 / 10	—	Last set Killer
Biceps	Bicep Curl	15 / 12	20 / 12	25 / 10	30 / 10	15 / 12	tight, tight
Triceps	Tricep Extension	15 / 12	20 / 10	25 / 10	30 / 10	15 / 12	matches high
chest	Fly	—	30 / 10	30 / 10	30 / 10	20 / 10	Less sore

CARDIO ACTIVITY

Type of Exercise	Warm Up Period	Sustained Heart Rate	Workout Period In Sustained Heart Rate	Cooldown Period
Cycle	5	140	10	5
Run	5	155	35	5
Cycle	5	140	10	5

Record your daily intake of calories, carbohydrates, and proteins, and list your weight

DIET

Day's Calories	Carbohydrates	Protein	Weight
1800	800	250	133

SUCCESS/DISAPPOINTMENT OF THE DAY

Nice, long run.

Note the day's successes and/or disappointments

Overall Grade: (A) | B | C | D | F   How I felt today: Exhausted | Slow | Average | (Strong) | Unstoppable

Grade your day from A to F

Sum up how you felt overall each day

WEEK 1 Inspiration: SERENA WILLIAMS

Tennis legend who transformed the women's game

MONDAY	DATE

VITAL STATS: Hometown: Saginaw, Michigan
Born: September 26, 1981
Height: 5 ft 9 in / 175 cm Weight: 155 lb / 70 kg

GOAL FOR THE DAY

RESISTANCE TRAINING

Muscle Group	Exercise	Warm-Up	Set 1	Set 2	Set 3	Cooldown	Comments

CARDIO ACTIVITY

Type of Exercise	Warm-Up Period	Sustained Heart Rate	Workout Period In Sustained Heart Rate	Cooldown Period

DIET

Day's Calories	Carbohydrates	Protein	Weight

SUCCESS/DISAPPOINTMENT OF THE DAY

FOCUS

Overall Grade: **A** | **B** | **C** | **D** | **F** How I felt today: **Exhausted** | **Slow** | **Average** | **Strong** | **Unstoppable**

SERENA WILLIAMS is not just one of the greatest tennis players of all time; her combination of power and athleticism revolutionized the women's game. She is also one of the most mentally tough athletes of her era, having won numerous games after being down match points, as well as battling back from several career-threatening injuries. Her success and longevity are great advertisements for the benefits of hard work and dedication.

TUESDAY	DATE

GOAL FOR THE DAY

RESISTANCE TRAINING

Muscle Group	Exercise	Warm-Up	Set 1	Set 2	Set 3	Cooldown	Comments

CARDIO ACTIVITY

Type of Exercise	Warm-Up Period	Sustained Heart Rate	Workout Period In Sustained Heart Rate	Cooldown Period

DIET

Day's Calories	Carbohydrates	Protein	Weight

SUCCESS/DISAPPOINTMENT OF THE DAY

Overall Grade: **A** | **B** | **C** | **D** | **F** How I felt today: **Exhausted** | **Slow** | **Average** | **Strong** | **Unstoppable**

WILLIAMS ON
LUCK

WEDNESDAY | DATE

"Luck has nothing to do with it, because I have spent many, many hours, countless hours, on the court working for my one moment in time, not knowing when it would come."

GOAL FOR THE DAY

RESISTANCE TRAINING

Muscle Group	Exercise	Warm-Up	Set 1	Set 2	Set 3	Cooldown	Comments

CARDIO ACTIVITY

Type of Exercise	Warm-Up Period	Sustained Heart Rate	Workout Period In Sustained Heart Rate	Cooldown Period

DIET

Day's Calories	Carbohydrates	Protein	Weight

SUCCESS/DISAPPOINTMENT OF THE DAY

CHALLENGE

Overall Grade: **A** | **B** | **C** | **D** | **F** How I felt today: **Exhausted** | **Slow** | **Average** | **Strong** | **Unstoppable**

WILLIAMS ON
FIGHTING

THURSDAY	DATE

"I've always been a fighter and I've always fought through things my whole life."

GOAL FOR THE DAY

RESISTANCE TRAINING

Muscle Group	Exercise	Warm-Up	Set 1	Set 2	Set 3	Cooldown	Comments

CARDIO ACTIVITY

Type of Exercise	Warm-Up Period	Sustained Heart Rate	Workout Period In Sustained Heart Rate	Cooldown Period

DIET

Day's Calories	Carbohydrates	Protein	Weight

SUCCESS/DISAPPOINTMENT OF THE DAY

Overall Grade: **A** | **B** | **C** | **D** | **F**   How I felt today: **Exhausted** | **Slow** | **Average** | **Strong** | **Unstoppable**

WILLIAMS ON
LOSING

FRIDAY	DATE

"If anything, you know, I think losing makes me even more motivated."

GOAL FOR THE DAY

RESISTANCE TRAINING

Muscle Group	Exercise	Warm-Up	Set 1	Set 2	Set 3	Cooldown	Comments

CARDIO ACTIVITY

Type of Exercise	Warm-Up Period	Sustained Heart Rate	Workout Period In Sustained Heart Rate	Cooldown Period

DIET

Day's Calories	Carbohydrates	Protein	Weight

SUCCESS/DISAPPOINTMENT OF THE DAY

PERSEVERE

Overall Grade: **A** | **B** | **C** | **D** | **F** How I felt today: **Exhausted** | **Slow** | **Average** | **Strong** | **Unstoppable**

WILLIAMS ON
NEVER GIVING UP

SATURDAY	DATE

"Everyone's dream can come true if you just stick to it and work hard."

GOAL FOR THE DAY

RESISTANCE TRAINING

Muscle Group	Exercise	Warm-Up	Set 1	Set 2	Set 3	Cooldown	Comments

CARDIO ACTIVITY

Type of Exercise	Warm-Up Period	Sustained Heart Rate	Workout Period In Sustained Heart Rate	Cooldown Period

DIET

Day's Calories	Carbohydrates	Protein	Weight

SUCCESS/DISAPPOINTMENT OF THE DAY

Overall Grade: **A** | **B** | **C** | **D** | **F** How I felt today: **Exhausted** | **Slow** | **Average** | **Strong** | **Unstoppable**

WILLIAMS ON
PERFECTIONISM

SUNDAY	DATE

"I'm a perfectionist. I'm pretty much insatiable. I feel there's so many things I can improve on."

GOAL FOR THE DAY

RESISTANCE TRAINING

Muscle Group	Exercise	Warm-Up	Set 1	Set 2	Set 3	Cooldown	Comments

CARDIO ACTIVITY

Type of Exercise	Warm-Up Period	Sustained Heart Rate	Workout Period In Sustained Heart Rate	Cooldown Period

DIET

Day's Calories	Carbohydrates	Protein	Weight

SACRIFICE

SUCCESS/DISAPPOINTMENT OF THE DAY

Overall Grade: **A** | **B** | **C** | **D** | **F**   How I felt today: **Exhausted** | **Slow** | **Average** | **Strong** | **Unstoppable**

WEEK 2 Inspiration: TONY AZEVEDO
Champion water polo player and Olympian

MONDAY	DATE

VITAL STATS: Hometown: Rio de Janeiro, Brazil
Born: November 21, 1981
Height: 6 ft 1 in / 185 cm Weight: 193 lb / 88 kg

GOAL FOR THE DAY

RESISTANCE TRAINING

Muscle Group	Exercise	Warm-Up	Set 1	Set 2	Set 3	Cooldown	Comments

CARDIO ACTIVITY

Type of Exercise	Warm-Up Period	Sustained Heart Rate	Workout Period In Sustained Heart Rate	Cooldown Period

DIET

Day's Calories	Carbohydrates	Protein	Weight

SUCCESS/DISAPPOINTMENT OF THE DAY

Overall Grade: **A** | **B** | **C** | **D** | **F** How I felt today: **Exhausted** | **Slow** | **Average** | **Strong** | **Unstoppable**

TUESDAY	DATE

A water polo star at Stanford University, **TONY AZEVEDO** is a four-time Pan American Games gold medalist. His dream of Olympic gold came tantalizingly close in 2008, winning silver in Beijing. As a child he competed in baseball, basketball, and swimming, but made the biggest splash in water polo. Azevedo maintains his sports background strengthened his arms, legs, and breathing. He claims to owe his success to a regimen of "surf and turf" training.

GOAL FOR THE DAY

RESISTANCE TRAINING

Muscle Group	Exercise	Warm-Up	Set 1	Set 2	Set 3	Cooldown	Comments

CARDIO ACTIVITY

Type of Exercise	Warm-Up Period	Sustained Heart Rate	Workout Period In Sustained Heart Rate	Cooldown Period

DIET

Day's Calories	Carbohydrates	Protein	Weight

SUCCESS/DISAPPOINTMENT OF THE DAY

BREAK THROUGH

Overall Grade: **A** | **B** | **C** | **D** | **F** How I felt today: **Exhausted** | **Slow** | **Average** | **Strong** | **Unstoppable**

WEDNESDAY DATE

"Water polo. ... [is] just like any other sport: the faster you are the easier it is."

GOAL FOR THE DAY

RESISTANCE TRAINING

Muscle Group	Exercise	Warm-Up	Set 1	Set 2	Set 3	Cooldown	Comments

CARDIO ACTIVITY

Type of Exercise	Warm-Up Period	Sustained Heart Rate	Workout Period In Sustained Heart Rate	Cooldown Period

DIET

Day's Calories	Carbohydrates	Protein	Weight

SUCCESS/DISAPPOINTMENT OF THE DAY

Overall Grade: **A** | **B** | **C** | **D** | **F**   How I felt today: **Exhausted** | **Slow** | **Average** | **Strong** | **Unstoppable**

AZEVEDO ON
DETERMINATION

THURSDAY	DATE

"I go out there and try to play hard every time."

GOAL FOR THE DAY

RESISTANCE TRAINING

Muscle Group	Exercise	Warm-Up	Set 1	Set 2	Set 3	Cooldown	Comments

CARDIO ACTIVITY

Type of Exercise	Warm-Up Period	Sustained Heart Rate	Workout Period In Sustained Heart Rate	Cooldown Period

DIET

Day's Calories	Carbohydrates	Protein	Weight

SUCCESS/DISAPPOINTMENT OF THE DAY

ACHIEVE

Overall Grade: **A** | **B** | **C** | **D** | **F** How I felt today: **Exhausted** | **Slow** | **Average** | **Strong** | **Unstoppable**

AZEVEDO ON MOTIVATION

FRIDAY	DATE

"It's the gold medal that drives me. I love the sport. I love playing with my teammates. It's so much fun out there. But there's one thing that keeps me out there training every day as hard as I can: I want to win a gold medal."

GOAL FOR THE DAY

RESISTANCE TRAINING

Muscle Group	Exercise	Warm-Up	Set 1	Set 2	Set 3	Cooldown	Comments

CARDIO ACTIVITY

Type of Exercise	Warm-Up Period	Sustained Heart Rate	Workout Period In Sustained Heart Rate	Cooldown Period

DIET

Day's Calories	Carbohydrates	Protein	Weight

SUCCESS/DISAPPOINTMENT OF THE DAY

Overall Grade: **A** | **B** | **C** | **D** | **F** How I felt today: **Exhausted** | **Slow** | **Average** | **Strong** | **Unstoppable**

AZEVEDO ON BEING CALLED THE MICHAEL JORDAN OF WATER POLO

SATURDAY	DATE

"I can't think I'm the Michael Jordan [of my sport]. If you think you're someone else, you have no room to improve. I can't think about it."

GOAL FOR THE DAY

RESISTANCE TRAINING

Muscle Group	Exercise	Warm-Up	Set 1	Set 2	Set 3	Cooldown	Comments

CARDIO ACTIVITY

Type of Exercise	Warm-Up Period	Sustained Heart Rate	Workout Period In Sustained Heart Rate	Cooldown Period

DIET

Day's Calories	Carbohydrates	Protein	Weight

SUCCESS/DISAPPOINTMENT OF THE DAY

SUCCESS

Overall Grade: **A** | **B** | **C** | **D** | **F** How I felt today: **Exhausted** | **Slow** | **Average** | **Strong** | **Unstoppable**

AZEVEDO ON
WORKING OUT

SUNDAY	DATE

"Water polo is an intense sport, so the type of workouts that you have to do must deal with a variety of muscles. Running is something that really helps the endurance. Also lifting weights and swimming hard are the obvious keys to becoming a great player."

GOAL FOR THE DAY

RESISTANCE TRAINING

Muscle Group	Exercise	Warm-Up	Set 1	Set 2	Set 3	Cooldown	Comments

CARDIO ACTIVITY

Type of Exercise	Warm-Up Period	Sustained Heart Rate	Workout Period In Sustained Heart Rate	Cooldown Period

DIET

Day's Calories	Carbohydrates	Protein	Weight

SUCCESS/DISAPPOINTMENT OF THE DAY

Overall Grade: **A** | **B** | **C** | **D** | **F** How I felt today: **Exhausted** | **Slow** | **Average** | **Strong** | **Unstoppable**

WEEK 3 Inspiration: DAVID BECKHAM

Soccer champion and former captain of Manchester United

MONDAY	DATE

VITAL STATS: Hometown: Leytonstone, UK
Born: May 2, 1975
Height: 5 ft 11 in / 180 cm Weight: 161 lb / 73 kg

GOAL FOR THE DAY

RESISTANCE TRAINING

Muscle Group	Exercise	Warm-Up	Set 1	Set 2	Set 3	Cooldown	Comments

CARDIO ACTIVITY

Type of Exercise	Warm-Up Period	Sustained Heart Rate	Workout Period In Sustained Heart Rate	Cooldown Period

DIET

Day's Calories	Carbohydrates	Protein	Weight

FINISH IT

SUCCESS/DISAPPOINTMENT OF THE DAY

Overall Grade: **A** | **B** | **C** | **D** | **F**   How I felt today: **Exhausted** | **Slow** | **Average** | **Strong** | **Unstoppable**

DAVID BECKHAM became a phenomenon in England during his play as a midfielder for Manchester United. The soccer sensation merged the charisma of a rock star with the agility of a first-rate athlete, equal parts Elvis and Pelé. Beckham is a virtually unstoppable force and is able to score goals from extreme distances: he has kicked a ball to score from 171 feet/52 meters. In 2007 Beckham crossed the Atlantic, joining LA Galaxy from Real Madrid. He ended his glorious career with Paris Saint-Germain in 2013, at the age of 38.

TUESDAY	DATE

GOAL FOR THE DAY

RESISTANCE TRAINING

Muscle Group	Exercise	Warm-Up	Set 1	Set 2	Set 3	Cooldown	Comments

CARDIO ACTIVITY

Type of Exercise	Warm-Up Period	Sustained Heart Rate	Workout Period In Sustained Heart Rate	Cooldown Period

DIET

Day's Calories	Carbohydrates	Protein	Weight

SUCCESS/DISAPPOINTMENT OF THE DAY

Overall Grade: **A** | **B** | **C** | **D** | **F** How I felt today: **Exhausted** | **Slow** | **Average** | **Strong** | **Unstoppable**

BECKHAM ON
PRACTICE AND THE PAYOFF

WEDNESDAY	DATE

"As soon as a free kick is given and it's anywhere near the box, I get excited. The crowd lifts themselves, and there's a buzz around the stadium. I know it's my turn for everyone to watch me. I practice this thirty, forty, fifty times a day in training, and when I do get the chance, I like to hit the target."

GOAL FOR THE DAY

RESISTANCE TRAINING

Muscle Group	Exercise	Warm-Up	Set 1	Set 2	Set 3	Cooldown	Comments

CARDIO ACTIVITY

Type of Exercise	Warm-Up Period	Sustained Heart Rate	Workout Period In Sustained Heart Rate	Cooldown Period

DIET

Day's Calories	Carbohydrates	Protein	Weight

WIN

SUCCESS/DISAPPOINTMENT OF THE DAY

Overall Grade: **A** | **B** | **C** | **D** | **F**   How I felt today: **Exhausted** | **Slow** | **Average** | **Strong** | **Unstoppable**

THURSDAY | DATE

"Play hard and win big. The more you train, the more you gain."

GOAL FOR THE DAY

RESISTANCE TRAINING

Muscle Group	Exercise	Warm-Up	Set 1	Set 2	Set 3	Cooldown	Comments

CARDIO ACTIVITY

Type of Exercise	Warm-Up Period	Sustained Heart Rate	Workout Period In Sustained Heart Rate	Cooldown Period

DIET

Day's Calories	Carbohydrates	Protein	Weight

SUCCESS/DISAPPOINTMENT OF THE DAY

Overall Grade: **A** | **B** | **C** | **D** | **F** How I felt today: **Exhausted** | **Slow** | **Average** | **Strong** | **Unstoppable**

BECKHAM ON
REACHING HIS PEAK

FRIDAY | DATE

"People do say that at twenty-eight you are at your peak, but I'd like to think I've got quite a bit more left in my legs. I think, ten, fifteen years ago, things were totally different, but nutrition and training have moved on so much. Nowadays, you've got to be fit to play at the top level, so that players last longer. I've definitely got the ambition to go on and win more trophies."

GOAL FOR THE DAY

RESISTANCE TRAINING

Muscle Group	Exercise	Warm-Up	Set 1	Set 2	Set 3	Cooldown	Comments

CARDIO ACTIVITY

Type of Exercise	Warm-Up Period	Sustained Heart Rate	Workout Period In Sustained Heart Rate	Cooldown Period

DIET

Day's Calories	Carbohydrates	Protein	Weight

EXCEL

SUCCESS/DISAPPOINTMENT OF THE DAY

Overall Grade: **A** | **B** | **C** | **D** | **F** How I felt today: **Exhausted** | **Slow** | **Average** | **Strong** | **Unstoppable**

BECKHAM ON THE CHALLENGE OF COMPETITION

SATURDAY	DATE

"You always want to test yourself against the best."

GOAL FOR THE DAY

Muscle Group	Exercise	Warm-Up	Set 1	Set 2	Set 3	Cooldown	Comments

RESISTANCE TRAINING

Type of Exercise	Warm-Up Period	Sustained Heart Rate	Workout Period In Sustained Heart Rate	Cooldown Period

CARDIO ACTIVITY

Day's Calories	Carbohydrates	Protein	Weight

DIET

SUCCESS/DISAPPOINTMENT OF THE DAY

Overall Grade: **A** | **B** | **C** | **D** | **F**   How I felt today: **Exhausted** | **Slow** | **Average** | **Strong** | **Unstoppable**

BECKHAM ON
DEDICATION TO THE SPORT

SUNDAY	DATE

"Of course, I love my family and I have a wonderful life, but football is everything for me."

GOAL FOR THE DAY

RESISTANCE TRAINING

Muscle Group	Exercise	Warm-Up	Set 1	Set 2	Set 3	Cooldown	Comments

CARDIO ACTIVITY

Type of Exercise	Warm-Up Period	Sustained Heart Rate	Workout Period In Sustained Heart Rate	Cooldown Period

DIET

Day's Calories	Carbohydrates	Protein	Weight

SUCCESS/DISAPPOINTMENT OF THE DAY

FIGHT

Overall Grade: **A** | **B** | **C** | **D** | **F** How I felt today: **Exhausted** | **Slow** | **Average** | **Strong** | **Unstoppable**

WEEK 4 Inspiration: MIA HAMM

World-champion soccer player

MONDAY | DATE

VITAL STATS: Hometown: Selma, Alabama
Born: March 17, 1972
Height: 5 ft 5 in / 165 cm Weight: 125 lb / 57 kg

GOAL FOR THE DAY

RESISTANCE TRAINING

Muscle Group	Exercise	Warm-Up	Set 1	Set 2	Set 3	Cooldown	Comments

CARDIO ACTIVITY

Type of Exercise	Warm-Up Period	Sustained Heart Rate	Workout Period In Sustained Heart Rate	Cooldown Period

DIET

Day's Calories	Carbohydrates	Protein	Weight

SUCCESS/DISAPPOINTMENT OF THE DAY

Overall Grade: **A** | **B** | **C** | **D** | **F** How I felt today: **Exhausted** | **Slow** | **Average** | **Strong** | **Unstoppable**

When **MIA HAMM** was fifteen, she became the youngest member of the USA national soccer team. Regarded as the best women's soccer player in the world, Hamm prefers to be a crucial part of a team, rather than a star. The University of North Carolina graduate is the undisputed role model for millions of little girls who have her poster pinned to their bedroom walls. Aware of the responsibility, she trains tirelessly.

TUESDAY	DATE

GOAL FOR THE DAY

RESISTANCE TRAINING

Muscle Group	Exercise	Warm-Up	Set 1	Set 2	Set 3	Cooldown	Comments

CARDIO ACTIVITY

Type of Exercise	Warm-Up Period	Sustained Heart Rate	Workout Period In Sustained Heart Rate	Cooldown Period

DIET

Day's Calories	Carbohydrates	Protein	Weight

STRENGTH

SUCCESS/DISAPPOINTMENT OF THE DAY

Overall Grade: **A** | **B** | **C** | **D** | **F** How I felt today: **Exhausted** | **Slow** | **Average** | **Strong** | **Unstoppable**

HAMM ON TALENT

WEDNESDAY	DATE

"Everyone has talent, and God gave me the athletic ability and competitiveness to go out there and push myself. It would be a disservice to myself if I couldn't be the best athlete and best person I could be."

GOAL FOR THE DAY

RESISTANCE TRAINING

Muscle Group	Exercise	Warm-Up	Set 1	Set 2	Set 3	Cooldown	Comments

CARDIO ACTIVITY

Type of Exercise	Warm-Up Period	Sustained Heart Rate	Workout Period In Sustained Heart Rate	Cooldown Period

DIET

Day's Calories	Carbohydrates	Protein	Weight

SUCCESS/DISAPPOINTMENT OF THE DAY

Overall Grade: **A** | **B** | **C** | **D** | **F** How I felt today: **Exhausted** | **Slow** | **Average** | **Strong** | **Unstoppable**

HAMM ON REWARDS

THURSDAY | DATE

"Soccer taught me motivation, time management, goal setting—all these abilities that outside of sports have made a huge difference in my life. It defined my self-esteem. It gave me very special friends. It helped with my education and took me to many different countries."

GOAL FOR THE DAY

RESISTANCE TRAINING

Muscle Group	Exercise	Warm-Up	Set 1	Set 2	Set 3	Cooldown	Comments

CARDIO ACTIVITY

Type of Exercise	Warm-Up Period	Sustained Heart Rate	Workout Period In Sustained Heart Rate	Cooldown Period

DIET

Day's Calories	Carbohydrates	Protein	Weight

FOCUS

SUCCESS/DISAPPOINTMENT OF THE DAY

Overall Grade: **A** | **B** | **C** | **D** | **F**   How I felt today: **Exhausted** | **Slow** | **Average** | **Strong** | **Unstoppable**

HAMM ON
RESILIENCY

FRIDAY	DATE

"When things are tough and bad, make it as simple as possible. It's natural for us to make everything overblown. 'Oh my God, I'm so bad.' You just have to focus and concentrate."

GOAL FOR THE DAY

RESISTANCE TRAINING

Muscle Group	Exercise	Warm-Up	Set 1	Set 2	Set 3	Cooldown	Comments

CARDIO ACTIVITY

Type of Exercise	Warm-Up Period	Sustained Heart Rate	Workout Period In Sustained Heart Rate	Cooldown Period

DIET

Day's Calories	Carbohydrates	Protein	Weight

SUCCESS/DISAPPOINTMENT OF THE DAY

Overall Grade: A | B | C | D | F How I felt today: **Exhausted** | **Slow** | **Average** | **Strong** | **Unstoppable**

HAMM ON
ACCOMPLISHMENT

SATURDAY	DATE

"I don't think I'd be anywhere without sports. It gave me the opportunities and the avenues to succeed."

GOAL FOR THE DAY

RESISTANCE TRAINING

Muscle Group	Exercise	Warm-Up	Set 1	Set 2	Set 3	Cooldown	Comments

CARDIO ACTIVITY

Type of Exercise	Warm-Up Period	Sustained Heart Rate	Workout Period In Sustained Heart Rate	Cooldown Period

DIET

Day's Calories	Carbohydrates	Protein	Weight

CHALLENGE

SUCCESS/DISAPPOINTMENT OF THE DAY

Overall Grade: **A** | **B** | **C** | **D** | **F** How I felt today: **Exhausted** | **Slow** | **Average** | **Strong** | **Unstoppable**

HAMM ON
BEING FEARED

SUNDAY	DATE

"That's always the player I wanted to become, the one the opposition is worried about."

GOAL FOR THE DAY

Muscle Group	Exercise	Warm-Up	Set 1	Set 2	Set 3	Cooldown	Comments

RESISTANCE TRAINING

Type of Exercise	Warm-Up Period	Sustained Heart Rate	Workout Period In Sustained Heart Rate	Cooldown Period

CARDIO ACTIVITY

Day's Calories	Carbohydrates	Protein	Weight

DIET

SUCCESS/DISAPPOINTMENT OF THE DAY

Overall Grade: **A** | **B** | **C** | **D** | **F** How I felt today: **Exhausted** | **Slow** | **Average** | **Strong** | **Unstoppable**

WEEK 5 Inspiration: NADIA COMANECI

Legendary gymnast and nine-time Olympic medalist

MONDAY DATE

Vital Stats: Hometown: Onesti, Romania
Born: November 12, 1961
Height: 4 ft 11 in / 150 cm Weight: 86 lb / 39 kg

GOAL FOR THE DAY

RESISTANCE TRAINING

Muscle Group	Exercise	Warm-Up	Set 1	Set 2	Set 3	Cooldown	Comments

CARDIO ACTIVITY

Type of Exercise	Warm-Up Period	Sustained Heart Rate	Workout Period In Sustained Heart Rate	Cooldown Period

DIET

Day's Calories	Carbohydrates	Protein	Weight

SUCCESS/DISAPPOINTMENT OF THE DAY

PERSEVERE

Overall Grade: **A** | **B** | **C** | **D** | **F** How I felt today: **Exhausted** | **Slow** | **Average** | **Strong** | **Unstoppable**

NADIA COMANECI is a former gymnast who captured three gold medals, along with seven perfect 10 scores, at the Montreal Olympics in 1976, while just 14 years old. She won two more Olympic golds in Moscow four years later, as well as two World Championship and nine European Championship gold medals, to cement her reputation as not just one of the greatest gymnasts of all time, but also one of the greatest athletes of the twentieth century. Born in Romania, and now a naturalized citizen of the US, Comaneci is the only person to have received the Olympic Order twice.

TUESDAY	DATE

GOAL FOR THE DAY

RESISTANCE TRAINING

Muscle Group	Exercise	Warm-Up	Set 1	Set 2	Set 3	Cooldown	Comments

CARDIO ACTIVITY

Type of Exercise	Warm-Up Period	Sustained Heart Rate	Workout Period In Sustained Heart Rate	Cooldown Period

DIET

Day's Calories	Carbohydrates	Protein	Weight

SUCCESS/DISAPPOINTMENT OF THE DAY

Overall Grade: **A** | **B** | **C** | **D** | **F**   How I felt today: **Exhausted** | **Slow** | **Average** | **Strong** | **Unstoppable**

COMANECI ON HARD WORK

WEDNESDAY | DATE

"Hard work has made it easy. That is my secret. That is why I win."

GOAL FOR THE DAY

RESISTANCE TRAINING

Muscle Group	Exercise	Warm-Up	Set 1	Set 2	Set 3	Cooldown	Comments

CARDIO ACTIVITY

Type of Exercise	Warm-Up Period	Sustained Heart Rate	Workout Period In Sustained Heart Rate	Cooldown Period

DIET

Day's Calories	Carbohydrates	Protein	Weight

SACRIFICE

SUCCESS/DISAPPOINTMENT OF THE DAY

Overall Grade: **A** | **B** | **C** | **D** | **F** How I felt today: **Exhausted** | **Slow** | **Average** | **Strong** | **Unstoppable**

COMANECI ON
NEVER SETTLING

THURSDAY	DATE

"I don't think perfection is something that exists."

GOAL FOR THE DAY

RESISTANCE TRAINING

Muscle Group	Exercise	Warm-Up	Set 1	Set 2	Set 3	Cooldown	Comments

CARDIO ACTIVITY

Type of Exercise	Warm-Up Period	Sustained Heart Rate	Workout Period In Sustained Heart Rate	Cooldown Period

DIET

Day's Calories	Carbohydrates	Protein	Weight

SUCCESS/DISAPPOINTMENT OF THE DAY

Overall Grade: **A** | **B** | **C** | **D** | **F** How I felt today: **Exhausted** | **Slow** | **Average** | **Strong** | **Unstoppable**

COMANECI ON
MAINTAINING FOCUS

FRIDAY | DATE

"I'm the kind of person who looks at what I'm doing now. I don't like to look back."

GOAL FOR THE DAY

RESISTANCE TRAINING

Muscle Group	Exercise	Warm-Up	Set 1	Set 2	Set 3	Cooldown	Comments

CARDIO ACTIVITY

Type of Exercise	Warm-Up Period	Sustained Heart Rate	Workout Period In Sustained Heart Rate	Cooldown Period

DIET

Day's Calories	Carbohydrates	Protein	Weight

SUCCESS/DISAPPOINTMENT OF THE DAY

BREAK THROUGH

Overall Grade: **A** | **B** | **C** | **D** | **F**   How I felt today: **Exhausted** | **Slow** | **Average** | **Strong** | **Unstoppable**

COMANECI ON
PERSEVERANCE

SATURDAY	DATE

"When you have something in your mind and you want to do it—that's the way I am—I just go for it."

GOAL **FOR THE DAY**

RESISTANCE TRAINING

Muscle Group	Exercise	Warm-Up	Set 1	Set 2	Set 3	Cooldown	Comments

CARDIO ACTIVITY

Type of Exercise	Warm-Up Period	Sustained Heart Rate	Workout Period In Sustained Heart Rate	Cooldown Period

DIET

Day's Calories	Carbohydrates	Protein	Weight

SUCCESS/DISAPPOINTMENT **OF THE DAY**

Overall Grade: **A** | **B** | **C** | **D** | **F**

How I felt today: **Exhausted** | **Slow** | **Average** | **Strong** | **Unstoppable**

COMANECI ON
KEYS TO SUCCESS

SUNDAY	DATE

"I am so good because I work very hard for it. Gymnastics requires grace above all, but also courage, perseverance, and hard work."

GOAL FOR THE DAY

RESISTANCE TRAINING

Muscle Group	Exercise	Warm-Up	Set 1	Set 2	Set 3	Cooldown	Comments

CARDIO ACTIVITY

Type of Exercise	Warm-Up Period	Sustained Heart Rate	Workout Period In Sustained Heart Rate	Cooldown Period

DIET

Day's Calories	Carbohydrates	Protein	Weight

SUCCESS/DISAPPOINTMENT OF THE DAY

ACHIEVE

Overall Grade: **A** | **B** | **C** | **D** | **F** How I felt today: **Exhausted** | **Slow** | **Average** | **Strong** | **Unstoppable**

WEEK 6 Inspiration: OSCAR DE LA HOYA

World champion boxer and Olympic medalist

MONDAY	DATE

VITAL STATS: Hometown: Los Angeles, CA
Born: February 4, 1973
Height: 5ft 11 in / 180 cm Weight: 154 lb / 70 kg

GOAL FOR THE DAY

RESISTANCE TRAINING

Muscle Group	Exercise	Warm-Up	Set 1	Set 2	Set 3	Cooldown	Comments

CARDIO ACTIVITY

Type of Exercise	Warm-Up Period	Sustained Heart Rate	Workout Period In Sustained Heart Rate	Cooldown Period

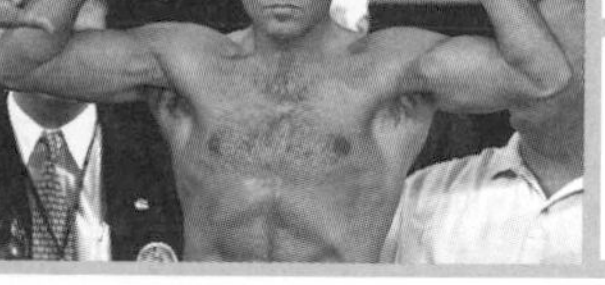

DIET

Day's Calories	Carbohydrates	Protein	Weight

SUCCESS/DISAPPOINTMENT OF THE DAY

Overall Grade: **A** | **B** | **C** | **D** | **F** How I felt today: **Exhausted** | **Slow** | **Average** | **Strong** | **Unstoppable**

Don't take **OSCAR DE LA HOYA** at face value: though model handsome, he's a fearsome fighter with a wicked left hand. Growing up, de la Hoya was bullied. Boxing, however, was in his genes. His grandfather and his father practiced "the sweet science," so Oscar turned to the neighborhood gym. Winning a gold medal at the 1992 Olympics, and following that with boxing championships, at ever-increasing weight levels, de la Hoya is the fight game's golden boy. While still active as a fighter, de la Hoya set up Golden Boy Promotions before retiring in 2009.

TUESDAY	DATE

GOAL FOR THE DAY

RESISTANCE TRAINING

Muscle Group	Exercise	Warm-Up	Set 1	Set 2	Set 3	Cooldown	Comments

CARDIO ACTIVITY

Type of Exercise	Warm-Up Period	Sustained Heart Rate	Workout Period In Sustained Heart Rate	Cooldown Period

DIET

Day's Calories	Carbohydrates	Protein	Weight

SUCCESS

SUCCESS/DISAPPOINTMENT OF THE DAY

Overall Grade: **A** | **B** | **C** | **D** | **F** How I felt today: **Exhausted** | **Slow** | **Average** | **Strong** | **Unstoppable**

DE LA HOYA ON
PUSHING HIMSELF

WEDNESDAY	DATE

"I feel strong, but there's always room for improvement."

GOAL FOR THE DAY

RESISTANCE TRAINING

Muscle Group	Exercise	Warm-Up	Set 1	Set 2	Set 3	Cooldown	Comments

CARDIO ACTIVITY

Type of Exercise	Warm-Up Period	Sustained Heart Rate	Workout Period In Sustained Heart Rate	Cooldown Period

DIET

Day's Calories	Carbohydrates	Protein	Weight

SUCCESS/DISAPPOINTMENT OF THE DAY

Overall Grade: **A** | **B** | **C** | **D** | **F**   How I felt today: **Exhausted** | **Slow** | **Average** | **Strong** | **Unstoppable**

DE LA HOYA ON
DEDICATION

THURSDAY	DATE

"It's in my blood. I sometimes say I hate the sport, but deep down inside I love it."

GOAL FOR THE DAY

RESISTANCE TRAINING

Muscle Group	Exercise	Warm-Up	Set 1	Set 2	Set 3	Cooldown	Comments

CARDIO ACTIVITY

Type of Exercise	Warm-Up Period	Sustained Heart Rate	Workout Period In Sustained Heart Rate	Cooldown Period

DIET

Day's Calories	Carbohydrates	Protein	Weight

SUCCESS/DISAPPOINTMENT OF THE DAY

FINISH IT

Overall Grade: **A** | **B** | **C** | **D** | **F** How I felt today: **Exhausted** | **Slow** | **Average** | **Strong** | **Unstoppable**

DE LA HOYA ON
BREAKING THROUGH THE WALL

FRIDAY	DATE

"I was getting lazy and I was getting tired. ... I would only train enough to beat the guy. Now, I'm training harder, training smarter; not just to beat the guy but to beat him decisively."

GOAL FOR THE DAY

RESISTANCE TRAINING

Muscle Group	Exercise	Warm-Up	Set 1	Set 2	Set 3	Cooldown	Comments

CARDIO ACTIVITY

Type of Exercise	Warm-Up Period	Sustained Heart Rate	Workout Period In Sustained Heart Rate	Cooldown Period

DIET

Day's Calories	Carbohydrates	Protein	Weight

SUCCESS/DISAPPOINTMENT OF THE DAY

Overall Grade: **A** | **B** | **C** | **D** | **F** How I felt today: **Exhausted** | **Slow** | **Average** | **Strong** | **Unstoppable**

DE LA HOYA ON HIS LEGACY

SATURDAY | DATE

"I'm fighting for history now, only history. In years to come, when people talk about the great fighters, I want my name to be one of the first that comes to their minds."

GOAL FOR THE DAY

RESISTANCE TRAINING

Muscle Group	Exercise	Warm-Up	Set 1	Set 2	Set 3	Cooldown	Comments

CARDIO ACTIVITY

Type of Exercise	Warm-Up Period	Sustained Heart Rate	Workout Period In Sustained Heart Rate	Cooldown Period

DIET

Day's Calories	Carbohydrates	Protein	Weight

WIN

SUCCESS/DISAPPOINTMENT OF THE DAY

Overall Grade: **A** | **B** | **C** | **D** | **F** How I felt today: **Exhausted** | **Slow** | **Average** | **Strong** | **Unstoppable**

DE LA HOYA ON TURNING MISTAKES INTO MOTIVATION

SUNDAY | DATE

"After a loss you feel down, and instead of blaming yourself, you blame everybody around you. I was blaming the whole world for my mistakes. I know I lost a couple of years because of my negativity, because I was not being truthful to myself. In those years I could have been a helluva fighter."

GOAL FOR THE DAY

RESISTANCE TRAINING

Muscle Group	Exercise	Warm-Up	Set 1	Set 2	Set 3	Cooldown	Comments

CARDIO ACTIVITY

Type of Exercise	Warm-Up Period	Sustained Heart Rate	Workout Period In Sustained Heart Rate	Cooldown Period

DIET

Day's Calories	Carbohydrates	Protein	Weight

SUCCESS/DISAPPOINTMENT OF THE DAY

Overall Grade: **A** | **B** | **C** | **D** | **F** How I felt today: **Exhausted** | **Slow** | **Average** | **Strong** | **Unstoppable**

WEEK 7 Inspiration: HAILE GEBRSELASSIE

Two-time Olympic medalist and world-record-breaking runner

MONDAY | DATE

VITAL STATS Hometown: Arsi, Ethiopia
Born: April 18, 1973
Height: 5 ft 3 in / 160 cm Weight: 123 lb / 56 kg

GOAL FOR THE DAY

RESISTANCE TRAINING

Muscle Group	Exercise	Warm-Up	Set 1	Set 2	Set 3	Cooldown	Comments

CARDIO ACTIVITY

Type of Exercise	Warm-Up Period	Sustained Heart Rate	Workout Period In Sustained Heart Rate	Cooldown Period

DIET

Day's Calories	Carbohydrates	Protein	Weight

EXCEL

SUCCESS/DISAPPOINTMENT OF THE DAY

Overall Grade: **A** | **B** | **C** | **D** | **F** How I felt today: **Exhausted** | **Slow** | **Average** | **Strong** | **Unstoppable**

HAILE GEBRSELASSIE had the ability to run at great speeds from an early age. Untutored, he ran on his own to see how far and how fast he could travel. The answers were very far and very, very fast. Gebrselassie has won two gold medals in track and field, first at the 1996 Olympics and later at the 2000 games. Remarkably, in 2008, at the age of 35, he won the Berlin Marathon in a world record time of 2:03.59; a mark which lasted for three yeras. Today, Gebrselassie strives to impart his wisdom onto the next generation of gold-getters.

TUESDAY | DATE

GOAL FOR THE DAY

RESISTANCE TRAINING

Muscle Group	Exercise	Warm-Up	Set 1	Set 2	Set 3	Cooldown	Comments

CARDIO ACTIVITY

Type of Exercise	Warm-Up Period	Sustained Heart Rate	Workout Period In Sustained Heart Rate	Cooldown Period

DIET

Day's Calories	Carbohydrates	Protein	Weight

SUCCESS/DISAPPOINTMENT OF THE DAY

Overall Grade: **A** | **B** | **C** | **D** | **F**   How I felt today: **Exhausted** | **Slow** | **Average** | **Strong** | **Unstoppable**

GEBRSELASSIE ON
ACHIEVEMENT

WEDNESDAY	DATE

"Sport has been great for me, a great learning place that if you want to achieve, you can, even if you are from the poorest part of Africa."

GOAL FOR THE DAY

RESISTANCE TRAINING

Muscle Group	Exercise	Warm-Up	Set 1	Set 2	Set 3	Cooldown	Comments

CARDIO ACTIVITY

Type of Exercise	Warm-Up Period	Sustained Heart Rate	Workout Period In Sustained Heart Rate	Cooldown Period

DIET

Day's Calories	Carbohydrates	Protein	Weight

SUCCESS/DISAPPOINTMENT OF THE DAY

FIGHT

Overall Grade: **A** | **B** | **C** | **D** | **F** How I felt today: **Exhausted** | **Slow** | **Average** | **Strong** | **Unstoppable**

GEBRSELASSIE ON NATURAL TRAINING

THURSDAY | DATE

"I used to run to school, 10k every day. Perfect preparation, really. In the rainy season, sometimes to get to the first lesson we had to run really quick, because we had to cross the river to school and we'd have to go up and down the bank to find a place to cross because there is no bridge."

GOAL FOR THE DAY

RESISTANCE TRAINING

Muscle Group	Exercise	Warm-Up	Set 1	Set 2	Set 3	Cooldown	Comments

CARDIO ACTIVITY

Type of Exercise	Warm-Up Period	Sustained Heart Rate	Workout Period In Sustained Heart Rate	Cooldown Period

DIET

Day's Calories	Carbohydrates	Protein	Weight

SUCCESS/DISAPPOINTMENT OF THE DAY

Overall Grade: **A** | **B** | **C** | **D** | **F**   How I felt today: **Exhausted** | **Slow** | **Average** | **Strong** | **Unstoppable**

GEBRSELASSIE ON THE MODERN AGE

"Driving makes you lazy."

FRIDAY | DATE

GOAL FOR THE DAY

RESISTANCE TRAINING

Muscle Group	Exercise	Warm-Up	Set 1	Set 2	Set 3	Cooldown	Comments

CARDIO ACTIVITY

Type of Exercise	Warm-Up Period	Sustained Heart Rate	Workout Period In Sustained Heart Rate	Cooldown Period

DIET

Day's Calories	Carbohydrates	Protein	Weight

SUCCESS/DISAPPOINTMENT OF THE DAY

STRENGTH

Overall Grade: **A** | **B** | **C** | **D** | **F**   How I felt today: **Exhausted** | **Slow** | **Average** | **Strong** | **Unstoppable**

GEBRSELASSIE ON PUSHING YOURSELF

SATURDAY	DATE

"For me, training is very difficult. Competition is easy."

GOAL FOR THE DAY

RESISTANCE TRAINING

Muscle Group	Exercise	Warm-Up	Set 1	Set 2	Set 3	Cooldown	Comments

CARDIO ACTIVITY

Type of Exercise	Warm-Up Period	Sustained Heart Rate	Workout Period In Sustained Heart Rate	Cooldown Period

DIET

Day's Calories	Carbohydrates	Protein	Weight

SUCCESS/DISAPPOINTMENT OF THE DAY

Overall Grade: **A** | **B** | **C** | **D** | **F** How I felt today: **Exhausted** | **Slow** | **Average** | **Strong** | **Unstoppable**

GEBRSELASSIE ON MOTIVATION

SUNDAY	DATE

"I run for myself and the people of Ethiopia. People push you very hard. They like me if I win. But when you run for a world record, it's not an easy job. People expect a world record from me, so I run for my people, my friends. I have to do something for them. I can run for myself, too, but I run for the people."

GOAL FOR THE DAY

RESISTANCE TRAINING

Muscle Group	Exercise	Warm-Up	Set 1	Set 2	Set 3	Cooldown	Comments

CARDIO ACTIVITY

Type of Exercise	Warm-Up Period	Sustained Heart Rate	Workout Period In Sustained Heart Rate	Cooldown Period

DIET

Day's Calories	Carbohydrates	Protein	Weight

SUCCESS/DISAPPOINTMENT OF THE DAY

FOCUS

Overall Grade: **A** | **B** | **C** | **D** | **F** How I felt today: **Exhausted** | **Slow** | **Average** | **Strong** | **Unstoppable**

WEEK 8 Inspiration: CARLI LLOYD

World-champion soccer player

MONDAY	DATE

VITAL STATS: Hometown: Delran Township, NJ
Born: July 16, 1982
Height: 5 ft 7 in / 170 cm Weight: 141 lb / 64 kg

GOAL FOR THE DAY

RESISTANCE TRAINING

Muscle Group	Exercise	Warm-Up	Set 1	Set 2	Set 3	Cooldown	Comments

CARDIO ACTIVITY

Type of Exercise	Warm-Up Period	Sustained Heart Rate	Workout Period In Sustained Heart Rate	Cooldown Period

DIET

Day's Calories	Carbohydrates	Protein	Weight

SUCCESS/DISAPPOINTMENT OF THE DAY

Overall Grade: **A** | **B** | **C** | **D** | **F** How I felt today: **Exhausted** | **Slow** | **Average** | **Strong** | **Unstoppable**

CARLI LLOYD is a pivotal force in the success of the US women's soccer team. She scored a 16-minute hat trick against Japan in the 2015 World Cup final and the decisive goals in winning gold in both the 2008 and 2012 Olympics. Lloyd attacks from midfield with relentless force and accuracy in front of goal. She showed signs of talent and hard work from a very young age, and has never let up.

TUESDAY	DATE

GOAL FOR THE DAY

RESISTANCE TRAINING

Muscle Group	Exercise	Warm-Up	Set 1	Set 2	Set 3	Cooldown	Comments

CARDIO ACTIVITY

Type of Exercise	Warm-Up Period	Sustained Heart Rate	Workout Period In Sustained Heart Rate	Cooldown Period

DIET

Day's Calories	Carbohydrates	Protein	Weight

CHALLENGE

SUCCESS/DISAPPOINTMENT OF THE DAY

Overall Grade: **A** | **B** | **C** | **D** | **F** How I felt today: **Exhausted** | **Slow** | **Average** | **Strong** | **Unstoppable**

LLOYD ON
PRACTICE AND PERSEVERENCE

WEDNESDAY | DATE

"I was just on a mission to help my team win this game. . . . Personally I have worked my butt off, and all the repetitions came into play."

GOAL FOR THE DAY

RESISTANCE TRAINING

Muscle Group	Exercise	Warm-Up	Set 1	Set 2	Set 3	Cooldown	Comments

CARDIO ACTIVITY

Type of Exercise	Warm-Up Period	Sustained Heart Rate	Workout Period In Sustained Heart Rate	Cooldown Period

DIET

Day's Calories	Carbohydrates	Protein	Weight

SUCCESS/DISAPPOINTMENT OF THE DAY

Overall Grade: **A** | **B** | **C** | **D** | **F** How I felt today: **Exhausted** | **Slow** | **Average** | **Strong** | **Unstoppable**

LLOYD ON INSTINCT

THURSDAY	DATE

"When you're feeling good mentally and physically, those plays are just instincts. . . . It just happens."

GOAL FOR THE DAY

RESISTANCE TRAINING

Muscle Group	Exercise	Warm-Up	Set 1	Set 2	Set 3	Cooldown	Comments

CARDIO ACTIVITY

Type of Exercise	Warm-Up Period	Sustained Heart Rate	Workout Period In Sustained Heart Rate	Cooldown Period

DIET

Day's Calories	Carbohydrates	Protein	Weight

PERSEVERE

SUCCESS/DISAPPOINTMENT OF THE DAY

Overall Grade: **A** | **B** | **C** | **D** | **F** How I felt today: **Exhausted** | **Slow** | **Average** | **Strong** | **Unstoppable**

LLOYD ON
BREAKING THROUGH WALLS

FRIDAY	DATE

"The harder you work and the more prepared you are for something, you're going to be able to persevere through anything."

GOAL FOR THE DAY

Muscle Group	Exercise	Warm-Up	Set 1	Set 2	Set 3	Cooldown	Comments

RESISTANCE TRAINING

Type of Exercise	Warm-Up Period	Sustained Heart Rate	Workout Period In Sustained Heart Rate	Cooldown Period

CARDIO ACTIVITY

Day's Calories	Carbohydrates	Protein	Weight

DIET

SUCCESS/DISAPPOINTMENT OF THE DAY

Overall Grade: **A** | **B** | **C** | **D** | **F** How I felt today: **Exhausted** | **Slow** | **Average** | **Strong** | **Unstoppable**

LLOYD ON
TRAINING FOR BIG MOMENTS

SATURDAY	DATE

"Everything that goes into my training, it's for those big moments and the mentality of continuing to train like an underdog and just to continue to put in the work is kind of what keeps me going."

GOAL FOR THE DAY

RESISTANCE TRAINING

Muscle Group	Exercise	Warm-Up	Set 1	Set 2	Set 3	Cooldown	Comments

CARDIO ACTIVITY

Type of Exercise	Warm-Up Period	Sustained Heart Rate	Workout Period In Sustained Heart Rate	Cooldown Period

DIET

Day's Calories	Carbohydrates	Protein	Weight

SUCCESS/DISAPPOINTMENT OF THE DAY

SACRIFICE

Overall Grade: **A** | **B** | **C** | **D** | **F** How I felt today: **Exhausted** | **Slow** | **Average** | **Strong** | **Unstoppable**

LLOYD ON
MENTAL TOUGHNESS

SUNDAY	DATE

"I visualized playing in a World Cup final and scoring four goals. It sounds pretty funny, but that's what it's all about. At the end of the day, you can be physically strong, you can have all the tools out there, but if your mental state isn't good enough, you can't bring yourself to bigger and better things."

GOAL FOR THE DAY

RESISTANCE TRAINING

Muscle Group	Exercise	Warm-Up	Set 1	Set 2	Set 3	Cooldown	Comments

CARDIO ACTIVITY

Type of Exercise	Warm-Up Period	Sustained Heart Rate	Workout Period In Sustained Heart Rate	Cooldown Period

DIET

Day's Calories	Carbohydrates	Protein	Weight

SUCCESS/DISAPPOINTMENT OF THE DAY

Overall Grade: **A** | **B** | **C** | **D** | **F** How I felt today: **Exhausted** | **Slow** | **Average** | **Strong** | **Unstoppable**

WEEK 9 Inspiration: USAIN BOLT

Sprinting legend, global icon and "World's Fastest Human"

MONDAY | DATE

VITAL STATS: Hometown: Trelawny, Jamaica
Born: August 21, 1986
Height: 6 ft 5 in / 196 cm Weight: 207 lb / 94 kg

GOAL FOR THE DAY

RESISTANCE TRAINING

Muscle Group	Exercise	Warm-Up	Set 1	Set 2	Set 3	Cooldown	Comments

CARDIO ACTIVITY

Type of Exercise	Warm-Up Period	Sustained Heart Rate	Workout Period In Sustained Heart Rate	Cooldown Period

DIET

Day's Calories	Carbohydrates	Protein	Weight

SUCCESS/DISAPPOINTMENT OF THE DAY

BREAK THROUGH

Overall Grade: **A** | **B** | **C** | **D** | **F** How I felt today: **Exhausted** | **Slow** | **Average** | **Strong** | **Unstoppable**

USAIN BOLT is a phenomenon: arguably the greatest athlete on the planet. All logic says that a man standing 6 ft 5 in, weighing 207 lb should not be able to run like the wind but that is exactly what Bolt does, smashing world records in the 100m (9.58secs) and 200m (19.19secs) and becoming the first man to win six Olympic sprinting golds. Bolt's laid-back attitude and showmanship on the track, firing "lightning bolts" out to his fans, belies a focused training ethic and fierce competitive drive.

TUESDAY | DATE

GOAL FOR THE DAY

RESISTANCE TRAINING

Muscle Group	Exercise	Warm-Up	Set 1	Set 2	Set 3	Cooldown	Comments

CARDIO ACTIVITY

Type of Exercise	Warm-Up Period	Sustained Heart Rate	Workout Period In Sustained Heart Rate	Cooldown Period

DIET

Day's Calories	Carbohydrates	Protein	Weight

SUCCESS/DISAPPOINTMENT OF THE DAY

Overall Grade: **A** | **B** | **C** | **D** | **F** How I felt today: **Exhausted** | **Slow** | **Average** | **Strong** | **Unstoppable**

WEDNESDAY | DATE

"I've worked hard over the years, I've been injured and I've worked through it, and I've made it."

GOAL FOR THE DAY

RESISTANCE TRAINING

Muscle Group	Exercise	Warm-Up	Set 1	Set 2	Set 3	Cooldown	Comments

CARDIO ACTIVITY

Type of Exercise	Warm-Up Period	Sustained Heart Rate	Workout Period In Sustained Heart Rate	Cooldown Period

DIET

Day's Calories	Carbohydrates	Protein	Weight

ACHIEVE

SUCCESS/DISAPPOINTMENT OF THE DAY

Overall Grade: **A** | **B** | **C** | **D** | **F**   How I felt today: **Exhausted** | **Slow** | **Average** | **Strong** | **Unstoppable**

THURSDAY | DATE

"As long as I'm in great shape, nobody beats me, for sure."

GOAL FOR THE DAY

RESISTANCE TRAINING

Muscle Group	Exercise	Warm-Up	Set 1	Set 2	Set 3	Cooldown	Comments

CARDIO ACTIVITY

Type of Exercise	Warm-Up Period	Sustained Heart Rate	Workout Period In Sustained Heart Rate	Cooldown Period

DIET

Day's Calories	Carbohydrates	Protein	Weight

SUCCESS/DISAPPOINTMENT OF THE DAY

Overall Grade: **A** | **B** | **C** | **D** | **F**   How I felt today: **Exhausted** | **Slow** | **Average** | **Strong** | **Unstoppable**

BOLT ON
OVER THINKING

FRIDAY	DATE

"If you think about racing too much you may just lose it a little bit."

GOAL FOR THE DAY

RESISTANCE TRAINING

Muscle Group	Exercise	Warm-Up	Set 1	Set 2	Set 3	Cooldown	Comments

CARDIO ACTIVITY

Type of Exercise	Warm-Up Period	Sustained Heart Rate	Workout Period In Sustained Heart Rate	Cooldown Period

DIET

Day's Calories	Carbohydrates	Protein	Weight

SUCCESS/DISAPPOINTMENT OF THE DAY

SUCCESS

Overall Grade: **A** | **B** | **C** | **D** | **F** How I felt today: **Exhausted** | **Slow** | **Average** | **Strong** | **Unstoppable**

BOLT ON SETTING GOALS

SATURDAY	DATE

"I don't think limits."

GOAL FOR THE DAY

RESISTANCE TRAINING

Muscle Group	Exercise	Warm-Up	Set 1	Set 2	Set 3	Cooldown	Comments

CARDIO ACTIVITY

Type of Exercise	Warm-Up Period	Sustained Heart Rate	Workout Period In Sustained Heart Rate	Cooldown Period

DIET

Day's Calories	Carbohydrates	Protein	Weight

SUCCESS/DISAPPOINTMENT OF THE DAY

Overall Grade: **A** | **B** | **C** | **D** | **F** How I felt today: **Exhausted** | **Slow** | **Average** | **Strong** | **Unstoppable**

BOLT ON
GENETICS

SUNDAY	DATE

"My brother is really, really slow."

GOAL FOR THE DAY

RESISTANCE TRAINING

Muscle Group	Exercise	Warm-Up	Set 1	Set 2	Set 3	Cooldown	Comments

CARDIO ACTIVITY

Type of Exercise	Warm-Up Period	Sustained Heart Rate	Workout Period In Sustained Heart Rate	Cooldown Period

DIET

Day's Calories	Carbohydrates	Protein	Weight

SUCCESS/DISAPPOINTMENT OF THE DAY

FINISH IT

Overall Grade: **A** | **B** | **C** | **D** | **F** How I felt today: **Exhausted** | **Slow** | **Average** | **Strong** | **Unstoppable**

WEEK 10 Inspiration: MICHAEL JORDAN

Six-time NBA champion and five-time NBA Most Valuable Player

MONDAY	DATE

VITAL STATS: Hometown: Brooklyn, NY
Born: February 17, 1963
Height: 6 ft 6 in / 198 cm Weight: 216 lb / 98 kg

GOAL FOR THE DAY

RESISTANCE TRAINING

Muscle Group	Exercise	Warm-Up	Set 1	Set 2	Set 3	Cooldown	Comments

CARDIO ACTIVITY

Type of Exercise	Warm-Up Period	Sustained Heart Rate	Workout Period In Sustained Heart Rate	Cooldown Period

DIET

Day's Calories	Carbohydrates	Protein	Weight

SUCCESS/DISAPPOINTMENT OF THE DAY

Overall Grade: **A** | **B** | **C** | **D** | **F**   How I felt today: **Exhausted** | **Slow** | **Average** | **Strong** | **Unstoppable**

MICHAEL JORDAN was more than a basketball player—he was basketball. Embodying on-court aerial acrobatics, the onetime Chicago Bull soared above his competition. Winning MVP titles and championship rings was not enough for the hard-playing athlete. He pursued his dream of baseball, and though he never made it to the big leagues, he never regretted taking the chance, either. Jordan later returned to the hardwood court before finally hanging up his fabled number-23 jersey for good. His legend lives on.

TUESDAY	DATE

GOAL FOR THE DAY

RESISTANCE TRAINING

Muscle Group	Exercise	Warm-Up	Set 1	Set 2	Set 3	Cooldown	Comments

CARDIO ACTIVITY

Type of Exercise	Warm-Up Period	Sustained Heart Rate	Workout Period In Sustained Heart Rate	Cooldown Period

DIET

Day's Calories	Carbohydrates	Protein	Weight

SUCCESS/DISAPPOINTMENT OF THE DAY

WIN

Overall Grade: **A** | **B** | **C** | **D** | **F** How I felt today: **Exhausted** | **Slow** | **Average** | **Strong** | **Unstoppable**

JORDAN ON COMMITMENT

WEDNESDAY	DATE

"I'm not out there sweating for three hours every day just to find out what it feels like to sweat."

GOAL FOR THE DAY

RESISTANCE TRAINING

Muscle Group	Exercise	Warm-Up	Set 1	Set 2	Set 3	Cooldown	Comments

CARDIO ACTIVITY

Type of Exercise	Warm-Up Period	Sustained Heart Rate	Workout Period In Sustained Heart Rate	Cooldown Period

DIET

Day's Calories	Carbohydrates	Protein	Weight

SUCCESS/DISAPPOINTMENT OF THE DAY

Overall Grade: **A** | **B** | **C** | **D** | **F** How I felt today: **Exhausted** | **Slow** | **Average** | **Strong** | **Unstoppable**

JORDAN ON
HARD WORK AND ITS REWARDS

THURSDAY	DATE

"The game is my wife. It demands loyalty and responsibility, and it gives me back fulfillment and peace."

GOAL FOR THE DAY

RESISTANCE TRAINING

Muscle Group	Exercise	Warm-Up	Set 1	Set 2	Set 3	Cooldown	Comments

10

CARDIO ACTIVITY

Type of Exercise	Warm-Up Period	Sustained Heart Rate	Workout Period In Sustained Heart Rate	Cooldown Period

DIET

Day's Calories	Carbohydrates	Protein	Weight

EXCEL

SUCCESS/DISAPPOINTMENT OF THE DAY

Overall Grade: **A** | **B** | **C** | **D** | **F**   How I felt today: **Exhausted** | **Slow** | **Average** | **Strong** | **Unstoppable**

JORDAN ON SUCCESS

FRIDAY | DATE

"I've never been afraid to fail."

GOAL FOR THE DAY

RESISTANCE TRAINING

Muscle Group	Exercise	Warm-Up	Set 1	Set 2	Set 3	Cooldown	Comments

CARDIO ACTIVITY

Type of Exercise	Warm-Up Period	Sustained Heart Rate	Workout Period In Sustained Heart Rate	Cooldown Period

DIET

Day's Calories	Carbohydrates	Protein	Weight

SUCCESS/DISAPPOINTMENT OF THE DAY

Overall Grade: **A** | **B** | **C** | **D** | **F**   How I felt today: **Exhausted** | **Slow** | **Average** | **Strong** | **Unstoppable**

JORDAN ON
RETURNING TO BASKETBALL AFTER HIS BRIEF RETIREMENT

SATURDAY	DATE

"It's all about challenges and going out and seeing if I can achieve something. ... I'm just trying to play the game of basketball. If I can do it, great. If I can't, that's great too."

GOAL FOR THE DAY

RESISTANCE TRAINING

Muscle Group	Exercise	Warm-Up	Set 1	Set 2	Set 3	Cooldown	Comments

CARDIO ACTIVITY

Type of Exercise	Warm-Up Period	Sustained Heart Rate	Workout Period In Sustained Heart Rate	Cooldown Period

DIET

Day's Calories	Carbohydrates	Protein	Weight

FIGHT

SUCCESS/DISAPPOINTMENT OF THE DAY

Overall Grade: **A** | **B** | **C** | **D** | **F** How I felt today: **Exhausted** | **Slow** | **Average** | **Strong** | **Unstoppable**

JORDAN ON
BREAKING THROUGH THE WALL

SUNDAY	DATE

"Whenever I was working out and got tired and figured I ought to stop, I'd close my eyes and see that list [of players] in the locker room without my name on it, and that usually got me going again."

GOAL FOR THE DAY

RESISTANCE TRAINING

Muscle Group	Exercise	Warm-Up	Set 1	Set 2	Set 3	Cooldown	Comments

CARDIO ACTIVITY

Type of Exercise	Warm-Up Period	Sustained Heart Rate	Workout Period In Sustained Heart Rate	Cooldown Period

DIET

Day's Calories	Carbohydrates	Protein	Weight

SUCCESS/DISAPPOINTMENT OF THE DAY

Overall Grade: **A** | **B** | **C** | **D** | **F** How I felt today: **Exhausted** | **Slow** | **Average** | **Strong** | **Unstoppable**

WEEK 11 Inspiration: JACKIE JOYNER-KERSEE
Six-time Olympic medalist at track and field

MONDAY	DATE

VITAL STATS: Hometown: East St. Louis, Illinois
Born: March 3, 1962
Height: 5 ft 10 in / 178 cm Weight: 150 lb / 68 kg

GOAL FOR THE DAY

RESISTANCE TRAINING

Muscle Group	Exercise	Warm-Up	Set 1	Set 2	Set 3	Cooldown	Comments

CARDIO ACTIVITY

Type of Exercise	Warm-Up Period	Sustained Heart Rate	Workout Period In Sustained Heart Rate	Cooldown Period

DIET

Day's Calories	Carbohydrates	Protein	Weight

SUCCESS/DISAPPOINTMENT OF THE DAY

STRENGTH

Overall Grade: **A** | **B** | **C** | **D** | **F** How I felt today: **Exhausted** | **Slow** | **Average** | **Strong** | **Unstoppable**

TUESDAY	DATE

Asthma could have sidelined her; instead, it strengthened her resolve. At thirteen, **JACKIE JOYNER** saw the biopic of Babe Didrikson, an early women's champion at an array of sports, and vowed to become an all-around athlete. On a basketball scholarship to UCLA, Jackie met Coach Bob Kersee, whom she later married. Encouraged by him, she blazed through the grueling trials of the heptathlon. Scooping up competitive medals and sportsmanship awards, Jackie has gone the distance and left her mark as the "world's greatest female athlete."

GOAL FOR THE DAY

RESISTANCE TRAINING

Muscle Group	Exercise	Warm-Up	Set 1	Set 2	Set 3	Cooldown	Comments

CARDIO ACTIVITY

Type of Exercise	Warm-Up Period	Sustained Heart Rate	Workout Period In Sustained Heart Rate	Cooldown Period

DIET

Day's Calories	Carbohydrates	Protein	Weight

SUCCESS/DISAPPOINTMENT OF THE DAY

Overall Grade: **A** | **B** | **C** | **D** | **F**   How I felt today: **Exhausted** | **Slow** | **Average** | **Strong** | **Unstoppable**

JOYNER-KERSEE ON COMMITMENT

WEDNESDAY	DATE

"Never give up on yourself."

GOAL FOR THE DAY

RESISTANCE TRAINING

Muscle Group	Exercise	Warm-Up	Set 1	Set 2	Set 3	Cooldown	Comments

11

CARDIO ACTIVITY

Type of Exercise	Warm-Up Period	Sustained Heart Rate	Workout Period In Sustained Heart Rate	Cooldown Period

DIET

Day's Calories	Carbohydrates	Protein	Weight

FOCUS

SUCCESS/DISAPPOINTMENT OF THE DAY

Overall Grade: **A** | **B** | **C** | **D** | **F** How I felt today: **Exhausted** | **Slow** | **Average** | **Strong** | **Unstoppable**

JOYNER-KERSEE ON
FINDING A PURPOSE

THURSDAY	DATE

"You have to ask yourself, 'What is it that pulls your energy, what can you give of yourself?'"

GOAL FOR THE DAY

RESISTANCE TRAINING

Muscle Group	Exercise	Warm-Up	Set 1	Set 2	Set 3	Cooldown	Comments

CARDIO ACTIVITY

Type of Exercise	Warm-Up Period	Sustained Heart Rate	Workout Period In Sustained Heart Rate	Cooldown Period

DIET

Day's Calories	Carbohydrates	Protein	Weight

SUCCESS/DISAPPOINTMENT OF THE DAY

Overall Grade: **A** | **B** | **C** | **D** | **F** How I felt today: **Exhausted** | **Slow** | **Average** | **Strong** | **Unstoppable**

JOYNER-KERSEE ON MOTIVATION

FRIDAY	DATE

"All I ever wanted was to be able to compete. I don't take credit, because people came before me."

GOAL FOR THE DAY

RESISTANCE TRAINING

Muscle Group	Exercise	Warm-Up	Set 1	Set 2	Set 3	Cooldown	Comments

11

CARDIO ACTIVITY

Type of Exercise	Warm-Up Period	Sustained Heart Rate	Workout Period In Sustained Heart Rate	Cooldown Period

DIET

Day's Calories	Carbohydrates	Protein	Weight

SUCCESS/DISAPPOINTMENT OF THE DAY

CHALLENGE

Overall Grade: **A** | **B** | **C** | **D** | **F** How I felt today: **Exhausted** | **Slow** | **Average** | **Strong** | **Unstoppable**

JOYNER-KERSEE ON
ACHIEVEMENT

SATURDAY	DATE

"One thing I have in my favor is consistency. I've always asked that of myself. . . . Don't be a flash in the pan."

GOAL FOR THE DAY

RESISTANCE TRAINING

Muscle Group	Exercise	Warm-Up	Set 1	Set 2	Set 3	Cooldown	Comments

CARDIO ACTIVITY

Type of Exercise	Warm-Up Period	Sustained Heart Rate	Workout Period In Sustained Heart Rate	Cooldown Period

DIET

Day's Calories	Carbohydrates	Protein	Weight

SUCCESS/DISAPPOINTMENT OF THE DAY

Overall Grade: **A** | **B** | **C** | **D** | **F** How I felt today: **Exhausted** | **Slow** | **Average** | **Strong** | **Unstoppable**

JOYNER-KERSEE ON INSPIRATION

SUNDAY | DATE

"I was not one of the best girls on the team, but my goals and dreams were to improve myself each time I stepped out on the track."

GOAL FOR THE DAY

RESISTANCE TRAINING

Muscle Group	Exercise	Warm-Up	Set 1	Set 2	Set 3	Cooldown	Comments

CARDIO ACTIVITY

Type of Exercise	Warm-Up Period	Sustained Heart Rate	Workout Period In Sustained Heart Rate	Cooldown Period

DIET

Day's Calories	Carbohydrates	Protein	Weight

SUCCESS/DISAPPOINTMENT OF THE DAY

PERSEVERE

Overall Grade: **A** | **B** | **C** | **D** | **F**   How I felt today: **Exhausted** | **Slow** | **Average** | **Strong** | **Unstoppable**

WEEK 12 Inspiration: ALEXANDER KARELIN

World-champion wrestler and three-time Olympic medalist

MONDAY	DATE

VITAL STATS: Hometown: Novosibirsk, Siberia
Born: September 19, 1967
Height: 6 ft 4 in / 193 cm Weight: 295 lb / 134 kg

GOAL FOR THE DAY

RESISTANCE TRAINING

Muscle Group	Exercise	Warm-Up	Set 1	Set 2	Set 3	Cooldown	Comments

CARDIO ACTIVITY

Type of Exercise	Warm-Up Period	Sustained Heart Rate	Workout Period In Sustained Heart Rate	Cooldown Period

DIET

Day's Calories	Carbohydrates	Protein	Weight

SUCCESS/DISAPPOINTMENT OF THE DAY

Overall Grade: **A** | **B** | **C** | **D** | **F** How I felt today: **Exhausted** | **Slow** | **Average** | **Strong** | **Unstoppable**

ALEXANDER KARELIN'S opponents dubbed him "King Kong" and "the Experiment." There was something sci-fi-like about his thirteen-year undefeated run in Greco-Roman wrestling. When asked the secret of invincibility, the Russian replied he trained every day of his life, while nobody else knew the meaning of training. Karelin was overpowering on the international and Olympic circuit. Now retired, Karelin encourages children to pursue the noble sport. He likens an anticipation of victory to the sheerest form of happiness.

TUESDAY	DATE

GOAL FOR THE DAY

12

RESISTANCE TRAINING

Muscle Group	Exercise	Warm-Up	Set 1	Set 2	Set 3	Cooldown	Comments

CARDIO ACTIVITY

Type of Exercise	Warm-Up Period	Sustained Heart Rate	Workout Period In Sustained Heart Rate	Cooldown Period

DIET

Day's Calories	Carbohydrates	Protein	Weight

SACRIFICE

SUCCESS/DISAPPOINTMENT OF THE DAY

Overall Grade: **A** | **B** | **C** | **D** | **F** How I felt today: **Exhausted** | **Slow** | **Average** | **Strong** | **Unstoppable**

WEDNESDAY	DATE

"I train every day of my life as they have never trained a day in theirs."

GOAL FOR THE DAY

RESISTANCE TRAINING

Muscle Group	Exercise	Warm-Up	Set 1	Set 2	Set 3	Cooldown	Comments

CARDIO ACTIVITY

Type of Exercise	Warm-Up Period	Sustained Heart Rate	Workout Period In Sustained Heart Rate	Cooldown Period

DIET

Day's Calories	Carbohydrates	Protein	Weight

SUCCESS/DISAPPOINTMENT OF THE DAY

Overall Grade: **A** | **B** | **C** | **D** | **F**   How I felt today: **Exhausted** | **Slow** | **Average** | **Strong** | **Unstoppable**

KARELIN ON COMMITMENT

THURSDAY	DATE

"Strong people are always lucky (it's true) but to become the best in any field of human activity one should work hard."

GOAL FOR THE DAY

RESISTANCE TRAINING

Muscle Group	Exercise	Warm-Up	Set 1	Set 2	Set 3	Cooldown	Comments

CARDIO ACTIVITY

Type of Exercise	Warm-Up Period	Sustained Heart Rate	Workout Period In Sustained Heart Rate	Cooldown Period

DIET

Day's Calories	Carbohydrates	Protein	Weight

SUCCESS/DISAPPOINTMENT OF THE DAY

BREAK THROUGH

Overall Grade: **A** | **B** | **C** | **D** | **F** How I felt today: **Exhausted** | **Slow** | **Average** | **Strong** | **Unstoppable**

KARELIN ON
INTIMIDATION

FRIDAY	DATE

"I do not like to seem immodest, but. . . . I see fear in the eyes of most of my opponents."

GOAL FOR THE DAY

RESISTANCE TRAINING

Muscle Group	Exercise	Warm-Up	Set 1	Set 2	Set 3	Cooldown	Comments

CARDIO ACTIVITY

Type of Exercise	Warm-Up Period	Sustained Heart Rate	Workout Period In Sustained Heart Rate	Cooldown Period

DIET

Day's Calories	Carbohydrates	Protein	Weight

SUCCESS/DISAPPOINTMENT OF THE DAY

Overall Grade: **A** | **B** | **C** | **D** | **F**   How I felt today: **Exhausted** | **Slow** | **Average** | **Strong** | **Unstoppable**

KARELIN ON
OVERCOMING INJURY

SATURDAY	DATE

"I never thought of quitting. It just never crossed my mind. They would have had to carry me out on a stretcher for me to quit."

GOAL FOR THE DAY

RESISTANCE TRAINING

Muscle Group	Exercise	Warm-Up	Set 1	Set 2	Set 3	Cooldown	Comments

12

CARDIO ACTIVITY

Type of Exercise	Warm-Up Period	Sustained Heart Rate	Workout Period In Sustained Heart Rate	Cooldown Period

DIET

Day's Calories	Carbohydrates	Protein	Weight

ACHIEVE

SUCCESS/DISAPPOINTMENT OF THE DAY

Overall Grade: **A** | **B** | **C** | **D** | **F**   How I felt today: **Exhausted** | **Slow** | **Average** | **Strong** | **Unstoppable**

KARELIN ON MOTIVATION

SUNDAY	DATE

"All my rivals are strong, strong men but it doesn't frighten me. On the contrary, it stimulates me to work harder in training."

GOAL FOR THE DAY

RESISTANCE TRAINING

Muscle Group	Exercise	Warm-Up	Set 1	Set 2	Set 3	Cooldown	Comments

CARDIO ACTIVITY

Type of Exercise	Warm Up Period	Sustained Heart Rate	Workout Period In Sustained Heart Rate	Cooldown Period

DIET

Day's Calories	Carbohydrates	Protein	Weight

SUCCESS/DISAPPOINTMENT OF THE DAY

Overall Grade: **A** | **B** | **C** | **D** | **F** How I felt today: **Exhausted** | **Slow** | **Average** | **Strong** | **Unstoppable**

WEEK 13 Inspiration: MARIO LEMIEUX

Six-time National Hockey League scoring leader

MONDAY	DATE

VITAL STATS: Hometown: Montreal, Quebec
Born: October 5, 1965
Height: 6 ft 4 in / 193 cm Weight: 230 lb / 104 kg

GOAL FOR THE DAY

RESISTANCE TRAINING

Muscle Group	Exercise	Warm-Up	Set 1	Set 2	Set 3	Cooldown	Comments

CARDIO ACTIVITY

Type of Exercise	Warm-Up Period	Sustained Heart Rate	Workout Period In Sustained Heart Rate	Cooldown Period

DIET

Day's Calories	Carbohydrates	Protein	Weight

SUCCESS/DISAPPOINTMENT OF THE DAY

SUCCESS

Overall Grade: **A** | **B** | **C** | **D** | **F** How I felt today: **Exhausted** | **Slow** | **Average** | **Strong** | **Unstoppable**

Setting records, breaking barriers, **"SUPER MARIO" LEMIEUX'S** career with the Pittsburgh Penguins was seemingly charmed. After being diagnosed with a treatable form of Hodgkin's disease in 1993, he took one month off. Confidently stepping back on the ice on the evening of his last radiation treatment, he scored a goal and added an assist. He initially retired from the NHL in 1997, but returned to the Penguins as an owner/player in 2000, eventually retiring in 2006. Executive, athlete, philanthropist—a hat trick worth applauding.

TUESDAY	DATE

GOAL FOR THE DAY

RESISTANCE TRAINING

Muscle Group	Exercise	Warm-Up	Set 1	Set 2	Set 3	Cooldown	Comments

CARDIO ACTIVITY

Type of Exercise	Warm-Up Period	Sustained Heart Rate	Workout Period In Sustained Heart Rate	Cooldown Period

DIET

Day's Calories	Carbohydrates	Protein	Weight

SUCCESS/DISAPPOINTMENT OF THE DAY

Overall Grade: **A** | **B** | **C** | **D** | **F** How I felt today: **Exhausted** | **Slow** | **Average** | **Strong** | **Unstoppable**

WEDNESDAY	DATE

"I was always very competitive. Every time I stepped on the ice, I wanted to win."

GOAL FOR THE DAY

RESISTANCE TRAINING

Muscle Group	Exercise	Warm-Up	Set 1	Set 2	Set 3	Cooldown	Comments

CARDIO ACTIVITY

Type of Exercise	Warm-Up Period	Sustained Heart Rate	Workout Period In Sustained Heart Rate	Cooldown Period

DIET

Day's Calories	Carbohydrates	Protein	Weight

SUCCESS/DISAPPOINTMENT OF THE DAY

FINISH IT

Overall Grade: **A** | **B** | **C** | **D** | **F** How I felt today: **Exhausted** | **Slow** | **Average** | **Strong** | **Unstoppable**

LEMIEUX ON
MOTIVATION

THURSDAY DATE

"My job is to go on the ice and score some points. My goal is to win Stanley Cups."

GOAL FOR THE DAY

RESISTANCE TRAINING

Muscle Group	Exercise	Warm-Up	Set 1	Set 2	Set 3	Cooldown	Comments

CARDIO ACTIVITY

Type of Exercise	Warm-Up Period	Sustained Heart Rate	Workout Period In Sustained Heart Rate	Cooldown Period

DIET

Day's Calories	Carbohydrates	Protein	Weight

SUCCESS/DISAPPOINTMENT OF THE DAY

Overall Grade: **A** | **B** | **C** | **D** | **F** How I felt today: **Exhausted** | **Slow** | **Average** | **Strong** | **Unstoppable**

LEMIEUX ON SUCCESS

FRIDAY	DATE

"I set my standards high and I usually achieve them. I don't want to go out there and just play the game. I want to be the best. To do that, I need to be at the top of the scoring leaders."

GOAL FOR THE DAY

RESISTANCE TRAINING

Muscle Group	Exercise	Warm-Up	Set 1	Set 2	Set 3	Cooldown	Comments

CARDIO ACTIVITY

Type of Exercise	Warm-Up Period	Sustained Heart Rate	Workout Period In Sustained Heart Rate	Cooldown Period

DIET

Day's Calories	Carbohydrates	Protein	Weight

WIN

SUCCESS/DISAPPOINTMENT OF THE DAY

Overall Grade: **A** | **B** | **C** | **D** | **F** How I felt today: **Exhausted** | **Slow** | **Average** | **Strong** | **Unstoppable**

LEMIEUX ON
THE LOVE OF THE GAME

SATURDAY	DATE

"I've been playing this game for 25 years, since I was a little kid. It's always going to be in my blood."

GOAL FOR THE DAY

RESISTANCE TRAINING

Muscle Group	Exercise	Warm-Up	Set 1	Set 2	Set 3	Cooldown	Comments

CARDIO ACTIVITY

Type of Exercise	Warm-Up Period	Sustained Heart Rate	Workout Period In Sustained Heart Rate	Cooldown Period

DIET

Day's Calories	Carbohydrates	Protein	Weight

SUCCESS/DISAPPOINTMENT OF THE DAY

Overall Grade: **A** | **B** | **C** | **D** | **F**   How I felt today: **Exhausted** | **Slow** | **Average** | **Strong** | **Unstoppable**

LEMIEUX ON
MAKING A COMEBACK

SUNDAY	DATE

"A lot of people doubt that I can come back and be the player I was two years ago. That's motivation to me to come back and be as good as I was two years ago. I want to be the player I was, not just another player."

GOAL FOR THE DAY

RESISTANCE TRAINING

Muscle Group	Exercise	Warm-Up	Set 1	Set 2	Set 3	Cooldown	Comments

CARDIO ACTIVITY

Type of Exercise	Warm-Up Period	Sustained Heart Rate	Workout Period In Sustained Heart Rate	Cooldown Period

DIET

Day's Calories	Carbohydrates	Protein	Weight

SUCCESS/DISAPPOINTMENT OF THE DAY

EXCEL

Overall Grade: **A** | **B** | **C** | **D** | **F** How I felt today: **Exhausted** | **Slow** | **Average** | **Strong** | **Unstoppable**

WEEK 14 Inspiration: LENNOX LEWIS

Former undisputed heavyweight boxing champion of the world

MONDAY	DATE

VITAL STATS: Hometown: West Ham, England
Born: September 2, 1965
Height: 6 ft 5 in / 196 cm Weight: 247 lb / 112 kg

GOAL FOR THE DAY

RESISTANCE TRAINING

Muscle Group	Exercise	Warm-Up	Set 1	Set 2	Set 3	Cooldown	Comments

CARDIO ACTIVITY

Type of Exercise	Warm-Up Period	Sustained Heart Rate	Workout Period In Sustained Heart Rate	Cooldown Period

DIET

Day's Calories	Carbohydrates	Protein	Weight

SUCCESS/DISAPPOINTMENT OF THE DAY

Overall Grade: **A** | **B** | **C** | **D** | **F** How I felt today: **Exhausted** | **Slow** | **Average** | **Strong** | **Unstoppable**

LENNOX LEWIS saw sports as his ticket out of poverty. He used his intimidating size, strength, and smarts to crumple his opponents in the ring. Though he won silver and gold at the 1984 and 1988 Olympics, respectively, Lewis's professional ascent was not guaranteed. A fan of chess, Lewis had to checkmate the likes of Evander Holyfield and Mike Tyson to be coronated undisputed champ. Lewis reigned as a savvy, gentlemanly heavyweight king, always acknowledging that brains and brawn are both keys to sports success.

TUESDAY	DATE

GOAL FOR THE DAY

RESISTANCE TRAINING

Muscle Group	Exercise	Warm-Up	Set 1	Set 2	Set 3	Cooldown	Comments

CARDIO ACTIVITY

Type of Exercise	Warm-Up Period	Sustained Heart Rate	Workout Period In Sustained Heart Rate	Cooldown Period

DIET

Day's Calories	Carbohydrates	Protein	Weight

FIGHT

SUCCESS/DISAPPOINTMENT OF THE DAY

Overall Grade: **A** | **B** | **C** | **D** | **F** How I felt today: **Exhausted** | **Slow** | **Average** | **Strong** | **Unstoppable**

LEWIS ON
EXCELLENCE

WEDNESDAY	DATE

"It was always important to me to prove that I'm the best."

GOAL FOR THE DAY

RESISTANCE TRAINING

Muscle Group	Exercise	Warm-Up	Set 1	Set 2	Set 3	Cooldown	Comments

CARDIO ACTIVITY

Type of Exercise	Warm-Up Period	Sustained Heart Rate	Workout Period In Sustained Heart Rate	Cooldown Period

DIET

Day's Calories	Carbohydrates	Protein	Weight

SUCCESS/DISAPPOINTMENT OF THE DAY

Overall Grade: **A** | **B** | **C** | **D** | **F** How I felt today: **Exhausted** | **Slow** | **Average** | **Strong** | **Unstoppable**

LEWIS ON
GIVING IT YOUR ALL

THURSDAY	DATE

"If you can't give 110 percent, then you shouldn't do it—I've given 110 percent in my sport."

GOAL FOR THE DAY

14

RESISTANCE TRAINING

Muscle Group	Exercise	Warm-Up	Set 1	Set 2	Set 3	Cooldown	Comments

CARDIO ACTIVITY

Type of Exercise	Warm-Up Period	Sustained Heart Rate	Workout Period In Sustained Heart Rate	Cooldown Period

DIET

Day's Calories	Carbohydrates	Protein	Weight

STRENGTH

SUCCESS/DISAPPOINTMENT OF THE DAY

Overall Grade: **A** | **B** | **C** | **D** | **F** How I felt today: **Exhausted** | **Slow** | **Average** | **Strong** | **Unstoppable**

LEWIS ON ACCEPTING DEFEAT

FRIDAY	DATE

"I learned that defeat, properly handled, makes a person stronger."

GOAL FOR THE DAY

RESISTANCE TRAINING

Muscle Group	Exercise	Warm-Up	Set 1	Set 2	Set 3	Cooldown	Comments

14

CARDIO ACTIVITY

Type of Exercise	Warm-Up Period	Sustained Heart Rate	Workout Period In Sustained Heart Rate	Cooldown Period

DIET

Day's Calories	Carbohydrates	Protein	Weight

SUCCESS/DISAPPOINTMENT OF THE DAY

Overall Grade: **A** | **B** | **C** | **D** | **F** How I felt today: **Exhausted** | **Slow** | **Average** | **Strong** | **Unstoppable**

LEWIS ON
CHARACTER

SATURDAY | DATE

"The fundamental character traits of integrity, discipline and respect translate into a reward worth more than any purse."

GOAL FOR THE DAY

RESISTANCE TRAINING

Muscle Group	Exercise	Warm-Up	Set 1	Set 2	Set 3	Cooldown	Comments

CARDIO ACTIVITY

Type of Exercise	Warm-Up Period	Sustained Heart Rate	Workout Period In Sustained Heart Rate	Cooldown Period

DIET

Day's Calories	Carbohydrates	Protein	Weight

FOCUS

SUCCESS/DISAPPOINTMENT OF THE DAY

Overall Grade: **A** | **B** | **C** | **D** | **F** How I felt today: **Exhausted** | **Slow** | **Average** | **Strong** | **Unstoppable**

LEWIS ON
SURVIVAL IN THE RING

SUNDAY	DATE

"You have to remember, you're out there all alone and you have to know when to take chances and when not to. One punch can change everything. One punch and you're hanging on to survive and no one else can save you."

GOAL FOR THE DAY

RESISTANCE TRAINING

Muscle Group	Exercise	Warm-Up	Set 1	Set 2	Set 3	Cooldown	Comments

CARDIO ACTIVITY

Type of Exercise	Warm-Up Period	Sustained Heart Rate	Workout Period In Sustained Heart Rate	Cooldown Period

DIET

Day's Calories	Carbohydrates	Protein	Weight

SUCCESS/DISAPPOINTMENT OF THE DAY

Overall Grade: **A** | **B** | **C** | **D** | **F** How I felt today: **Exhausted** | **Slow** | **Average** | **Strong** | **Unstoppable**

WEEK 15 Inspiration: HERMANN MAIER
World-champion skier and two-time Olympic medalist

MONDAY | DATE

VITAL STATS: Hometown: Salzburg, Austria
Born: December 7, 1972
Height: 5 ft 9 in / 175 cm Weight: 190 lb / 86 kg

GOAL FOR THE DAY

RESISTANCE TRAINING

Muscle Group	Exercise	Warm-Up	Set 1	Set 2	Set 3	Cooldown	Comments

CARDIO ACTIVITY

Type of Exercise	Warm-Up Period	Sustained Heart Rate	Workout Period In Sustained Heart Rate	Cooldown Period

DIET

Day's Calories	Carbohydrates	Protein	Weight

SUCCESS/DISAPPOINTMENT OF THE DAY

CHALLENGE

Overall Grade: **A** | **B** | **C** | **D** | **F** How I felt today: **Exhausted** | **Slow** | **Average** | **Strong** | **Unstoppable**

He suffered spills, crashes, collisions, but he just kept going. No wonder Austrian skier **HERMANN MAIER** was known as "the Herminator." During a 13-year career, Maier amassed Olympic medals and World Cup titles, and did it while overcoming harrowing setbacks on and off the slopes. After Hermann was sidelined by a devastating motorcycle accident, his skiing future seemed in doubt. But with an iron will and a workout schedule that would make most mortals faint, it wasn't long before he was again speeding across finish lines.

TUESDAY | DATE

GOAL FOR THE DAY

RESISTANCE TRAINING

Muscle Group	Exercise	Warm-Up	Set 1	Set 2	Set 3	Cooldown	Comments

15

CARDIO ACTIVITY

Type of Exercise	Warm-Up Period	Sustained Heart Rate	Workout Period In Sustained Heart Rate	Cooldown Period

DIET

Day's Calories	Carbohydrates	Protein	Weight

SUCCESS/DISAPPOINTMENT OF THE DAY

Overall Grade: **A** | **B** | **C** | **D** | **F**   How I felt today: **Exhausted** | **Slow** | **Average** | **Strong** | **Unstoppable**

MAIER ON
BREAKING THROUGH THE WALL

WEDNESDAY	DATE

"I'm only happy when I'm skiing on the edge. It's the only place where I can be. If you're not there, well, forget about it."

GOAL FOR THE DAY

RESISTANCE TRAINING

Muscle Group	Exercise	Warm-Up	Set 1	Set 2	Set 3	Cooldown	Comments

CARDIO ACTIVITY

Type of Exercise	Warm-Up Period	Sustained Heart Rate	Workout Period In Sustained Heart Rate	Cooldown Period

DIET

Day's Calories	Carbohydrates	Protein	Weight

SUCCESS/DISAPPOINTMENT OF THE DAY

PERSEVERE

Overall Grade: **A** | **B** | **C** | **D** | **F** How I felt today: **Exhausted** | **Slow** | **Average** | **Strong** | **Unstoppable**

MAIER ON
MOTIVATION

THURSDAY	DATE

"I like to go fast. I like to win. If I lose, I'm not very happy."

GOAL FOR THE DAY

RESISTANCE TRAINING

Muscle Group	Exercise	Warm-Up	Set 1	Set 2	Set 3	Cooldown	Comments

CARDIO ACTIVITY

Type of Exercise	Warm-Up Period	Sustained Heart Rate	Workout Period In Sustained Heart Rate	Cooldown Period

DIET

Day's Calories	Carbohydrates	Protein	Weight

SUCCESS/DISAPPOINTMENT OF THE DAY

Overall Grade: **A** | **B** | **C** | **D** | **F**   How I felt today: **Exhausted** | **Slow** | **Average** | **Strong** | **Unstoppable**

MAIER ON
PERSEVERANCE

FRIDAY	DATE

"The moral of the story is you just can't give up. You got to keep on going if you want to be a success. Even as a kid, I always had to be the best. Second place made me angry."

GOAL FOR THE DAY

RESISTANCE TRAINING

Muscle Group	Exercise	Warm-Up	Set 1	Set 2	Set 3	Cooldown	Comments

15

CARDIO ACTIVITY

Type of Exercise	Warm-Up Period	Sustained Heart Rate	Workout Period In Sustained Heart Rate	Cooldown Period

DIET

Day's Calories	Carbohydrates	Protein	Weight

SUCCESS/DISAPPOINTMENT OF THE DAY

SACRIFICE

Overall Grade: **A** | **B** | **C** | **D** | **F** How I felt today: **Exhausted** | **Slow** | **Average** | **Strong** | **Unstoppable**

MAIER ON
ACHIEVEMENT

SATURDAY	DATE

"My lifelong dream has come true. I knew from the time I was eight that one day I would be champion—and that no one could stop me from achieving that."

GOAL FOR THE DAY

RESISTANCE TRAINING

Muscle Group	Exercise	Warm-Up	Set 1	Set 2	Set 3	Cooldown	Comments

CARDIO ACTIVITY

Type of Exercise	Warm-Up Period	Sustained Heart Rate	Workout Period In Sustained Heart Rate	Cooldown Period

DIET

Day's Calories	Carbohydrates	Protein	Weight

SUCCESS/DISAPPOINTMENT OF THE DAY

Overall Grade: **A** | **B** | **C** | **D** | **F** How I felt today: **Exhausted** | **Slow** | **Average** | **Strong** | **Unstoppable**

MAIER ON
CHALLENGES

SUNDAY	DATE

"To race as fast as I can race by race, one by one, is my only goal. My biggest goal is to just keep improving with each race."

GOAL **FOR THE DAY**

15

RESISTANCE TRAINING

Muscle Group	Exercise	Warm-Up	Set 1	Set 2	Set 3	Cooldown	Comments

CARDIO ACTIVITY

Type of Exercise	Warm-Up Period	Sustained Heart Rate	Workout Period In Sustained Heart Rate	Cooldown Period

DIET

Day's Calories	Carbohydrates	Protein	Weight

SUCCESS/DISAPPOINTMENT **OF THE DAY**

BREAK THROUGH

Overall Grade: **A** | **B** | **C** | **D** | **F** How I felt today: **Exhausted** | **Slow** | **Average** | **Strong** | **Unstoppable**

WEEK 16 Inspiration: MARIA SHARAPOVA

Russian tennis sensation, won Wimbledon at 17 years old.

MONDAY	DATE

VITAL STATS: Hometown: Nyagan, Russia
Born April 19, 1987
Height: 6 ft 2 in / 188 cm Weight: 130 lb / 59 kg

GOAL FOR THE DAY

RESISTANCE TRAINING

Muscle Group	Exercise	Warm-Up	Set 1	Set 2	Set 3	Cooldown	Comments

CARDIO ACTIVITY

Type of Exercise	Warm-Up Period	Sustained Heart Rate	Workout Period In Sustained Heart Rate	Cooldown Period

DIET

Day's Calories	Carbohydrates	Protein	Weight

SUCCESS/DISAPPOINTMENT OF THE DAY

Overall Grade: **A** | **B** | **C** | **D** | **F** How I felt today: **Exhausted** | **Slow** | **Average** | **Strong** | **Unstoppable**

MARIA SHARAPOVA was a precocious talent, turning professional at the age of fourteen. Where many young tennis sensations have experienced burnout, Sharapova has shown a remarkable resilience and strength throughout her career. She has overcome three serious shoulder injuries and spent many months on the sidelines. Despite this, she has won at least one singles title a year from 2003 through to 2015 and reached number 1 in the world on five separate occasions.

TUESDAY	DATE

GOAL FOR THE DAY

16

RESISTANCE TRAINING

Muscle Group	Exercise	Warm-Up	Set 1	Set 2	Set 3	Cooldown	Comments

CARDIO ACTIVITY

Type of Exercise	Warm-Up Period	Sustained Heart Rate	Workout Period In Sustained Heart Rate	Cooldown Period

DIET

Day's Calories	Carbohydrates	Protein	Weight

SUCCESS/DISAPPOINTMENT OF THE DAY

ACHIEVE

Overall Grade: **A** | **B** | **C** | **D** | **F** How I felt today: **Exhausted** | **Slow** | **Average** | **Strong** | **Unstoppable**

SHARAPOVA ON TRAINING SMARTER

WEDNESDAY | DATE

"I think 2013 showed me, like a few other years, how important being healthy is and how I must listen to my body. During this off-season I have been a little smarter on how I train and how I treat my body."

GOAL FOR THE DAY

RESISTANCE TRAINING

Muscle Group	Exercise	Warm-Up	Set 1	Set 2	Set 3	Cooldown	Comments

CARDIO ACTIVITY

Type of Exercise	Warm-Up Period	Sustained Heart Rate	Workout Period In Sustained Heart Rate	Cooldown Period

DIET

Day's Calories	Carbohydrates	Protein	Weight

SUCCESS/DISAPPOINTMENT OF THE DAY

Overall Grade: **A** | **B** | **C** | **D** | **F** How I felt today: **Exhausted** | **Slow** | **Average** | **Strong** | **Unstoppable**

SHARAPOVA ON FOCUS

THURSDAY | DATE

"When I walk through that gate to the court, that's my escape. I block out everything, good and bad."

GOAL FOR THE DAY

RESISTANCE TRAINING

Muscle Group	Exercise	Warm-Up	Set 1	Set 2	Set 3	Cooldown	Comments

CARDIO ACTIVITY

Type of Exercise	Warm-Up Period	Sustained Heart Rate	Workout Period In Sustained Heart Rate	Cooldown Period

DIET

Day's Calories	Carbohydrates	Protein	Weight

SUCCESS/DISAPPOINTMENT OF THE DAY

SUCCESS

Overall Grade: **A** | **B** | **C** | **D** | **F**   How I felt today: **Exhausted** | **Slow** | **Average** | **Strong** | **Unstoppable**

SHARAPOVA ON STAYING HEALTHY

FRIDAY	DATE

"My main goal is to stay healthy because when you're injured you realize how lucky you are to have your health."

GOAL FOR THE DAY

RESISTANCE TRAINING

Muscle Group	Exercise	Warm-Up	Set 1	Set 2	Set 3	Cooldown	Comments

CARDIO ACTIVITY

Type of Exercise	Warm-Up Period	Sustained Heart Rate	Workout Period In Sustained Heart Rate	Cooldown Period

DIET

Day's Calories	Carbohydrates	Protein	Weight

SUCCESS/DISAPPOINTMENT OF THE DAY

Overall Grade: **A** | **B** | **C** | **D** | **F** How I felt today: **Exhausted** | **Slow** | **Average** | **Strong** | **Unstoppable**

SHARAPOVA ON
CREATING HER OWN LEGACY

SATURDAY | DATE

"I'm not the next anyone, I'm the first Maria Sharapova."

GOAL FOR THE DAY

RESISTANCE TRAINING

Muscle Group	Exercise	Warm-Up	Set 1	Set 2	Set 3	Cooldown	Comments

16

CARDIO ACTIVITY

Type of Exercise	Warm-Up Period	Sustained Heart Rate	Workout Period In Sustained Heart Rate	Cooldown Period

DIET

Day's Calories	Carbohydrates	Protein	Weight

SUCCESS/DISAPPOINTMENT OF THE DAY

FINISH IT

Overall Grade: **A** | **B** | **C** | **D** | **F** How I felt today: **Exhausted** | **Slow** | **Average** | **Strong** | **Unstoppable**

SHARAPOVA ON GIVING HER ALL

SUNDAY	DATE

"Obviously, I felt a little tired but that's normal after playing four straight weeks. I mean, I'm not gonna feel great. My body's not gonna feel great. That's absolutely normal. But I just have to give it all I had, and I tried."

GOAL FOR THE DAY

RESISTANCE TRAINING

Muscle Group	Exercise	Warm-Up	Set 1	Set 2	Set 3	Cooldown	Comments

CARDIO ACTIVITY

Type of Exercise	Warm-Up Period	Sustained Heart Rate	Workout Period In Sustained Heart Rate	Cooldown Period

DIET

Day's Calories	Carbohydrates	Protein	Weight

SUCCESS/DISAPPOINTMENT OF THE DAY

Overall Grade: **A** | **B** | **C** | **D** | **F** How I felt today: **Exhausted** | **Slow** | **Average** | **Strong** | **Unstoppable**

WEEK 17 Inspiration: PAULA NEWBY-FRASER

World record-breaking triathlete

MONDAY | DATE

VITAL STATS: Hometown: Zimbabwe, Africa
Born: June 2, 1962
Height: 5 ft 4 in / 163 cm Weight: 125 lb / 57 kg

GOAL FOR THE DAY

RESISTANCE TRAINING

Muscle Group	Exercise	Warm-Up	Set 1	Set 2	Set 3	Cooldown	Comments

CARDIO ACTIVITY

Type of Exercise	Warm-Up Period	Sustained Heart Rate	Workout Period In Sustained Heart Rate	Cooldown Period

DIET

Day's Calories	Carbohydrates	Protein	Weight

SUCCESS/DISAPPOINTMENT OF THE DAY

SUCCESS

Overall Grade: **A** | **B** | **C** | **D** | **F**   How I felt today: **Exhausted** | **Slow** | **Average** | **Strong** | **Unstoppable**

PAULA NEWBY-FRASER is an athlete's athlete. She doesn't chase the microphones and isn't a household name, preferring to let her perseverance do the talking. An eight-time winner of the Ironman Triathlon in Hawaii and a multiple winner of ironman titles worldwide, she has swum, bicycled, and run with sore ankles, abscessed teeth, and symptoms of influenza. Competing into her forties, Paula analyzed her sport like a stockbroker, seeking the best return on her time's investment, with minimum injury and maximum fun.

TUESDAY	DATE

GOAL FOR THE DAY

RESISTANCE TRAINING

Muscle Group	Exercise	Warm-Up	Set 1	Set 2	Set 3	Cooldown	Comments

17

CARDIO ACTIVITY

Type of Exercise	Warm-Up Period	Sustained Heart Rate	Workout Period In Sustained Heart Rate	Cooldown Period

DIET

Day's Calories	Carbohydrates	Protein	Weight

SUCCESS/DISAPPOINTMENT OF THE DAY

Overall Grade: **A** | **B** | **C** | **D** | **F**   How I felt today: **Exhausted** | **Slow** | **Average** | **Strong** | **Unstoppable**

NEWBY-FRASER ON
TECHNIQUE

WEDNESDAY	DATE

"By training my body to rest at a high heart rate, I find I can recover quickly during races."

GOAL FOR THE DAY

RESISTANCE TRAINING

Muscle Group	Exercise	Warm-Up	Set 1	Set 2	Set 3	Cooldown	Comments

17

CARDIO ACTIVITY

Type of Exercise	Warm-Up Period	Sustained Heart Rate	Workout Period In Sustained Heart Rate	Cooldown Period

DIET

Day's Calories	Carbohydrates	Protein	Weight

WIN

SUCCESS/DISAPPOINTMENT OF THE DAY

Overall Grade: **A** | **B** | **C** | **D** | **F**   How I felt today: **Exhausted** | **Slow** | **Average** | **Strong** | **Unstoppable**

NEWBY-FRASER ON TRAINING

THURSDAY	DATE

"I never quit doing some semblance of strength training during the year. It's the foundation of everything I do in competition."

GOAL FOR THE DAY

RESISTANCE TRAINING

Muscle Group	Exercise	Warm-Up	Set 1	Set 2	Set 3	Cooldown	Comments

CARDIO ACTIVITY

Type of Exercise	Warm-Up Period	Sustained Heart Rate	Workout Period In Sustained Heart Rate	Cooldown Period

DIET

Day's Calories	Carbohydrates	Protein	Weight

SUCCESS/DISAPPOINTMENT OF THE DAY

Overall Grade: **A** | **B** | **C** | **D** | **F**   How I felt today: **Exhausted** | **Slow** | **Average** | **Strong** | **Unstoppable**

NEWBY-FRASER ON
MOTIVATION

FRIDAY | DATE

"I did this for pure enjoyment. Not many people can take their hobby, what they do as a passion, and mold it into a well-paying career. I've accomplished so much more than I could ever have dreamed of in triathlons."

GOAL FOR THE DAY

17

RESISTANCE TRAINING

Muscle Group	Exercise	Warm-Up	Set 1	Set 2	Set 3	Cooldown	Comments

CARDIO ACTIVITY

Type of Exercise	Warm-Up Period	Sustained Heart Rate	Workout Period In Sustained Heart Rate	Cooldown Period

DIET

Day's Calories	Carbohydrates	Protein	Weight

SUCCESS/DISAPPOINTMENT OF THE DAY

EXCEL

Overall Grade: **A** | **B** | **C** | **D** | **F** How I felt today: **Exhausted** | **Slow** | **Average** | **Strong** | **Unstoppable**

NEWBY-FRASER ON
DRIVE

SATURDAY	DATE

"When I first heard about triathlons in 1983, I looked at it and said, 'This is ridiculous.' It wasn't until I did a triathlon that I realized the allure of doing it, how addicted to it you can get."

GOAL FOR THE DAY

RESISTANCE TRAINING

Muscle Group	Exercise	Warm-Up	Set 1	Set 2	Set 3	Cooldown	Comments

CARDIO ACTIVITY

Type of Exercise	Warm-Up Period	Sustained Heart Rate	Workout Period In Sustained Heart Rate	Cooldown Period

DIET

Day's Calories	Carbohydrates	Protein	Weight

SUCCESS/DISAPPOINTMENT OF THE DAY

Overall Grade: **A** | **B** | **C** | **D** | **F**   How I felt today: **Exhausted** | **Slow** | **Average** | **Strong** | **Unstoppable**

NEWBY-FRASER ON ACHIEVEMENT

SUNDAY	DATE

"As much as people disbelieve this, I truly love what I do. It's challenging myself from year to year to see if I can rise to the occasion of trying to have a great race."

GOAL FOR THE DAY

RESISTANCE TRAINING

Muscle Group	Exercise	Warm-Up	Set 1	Set 2	Set 3	Cooldown	Comments

17

CARDIO ACTIVITY

Type of Exercise	Warm-Up Period	Sustained Heart Rate	Workout Period In Sustained Heart Rate	Cooldown Period

DIET

Day's Calories	Carbohydrates	Protein	Weight

FIGHT

SUCCESS/DISAPPOINTMENT OF THE DAY

Overall Grade: **A** | **B** | **C** | **D** | **F** How I felt today: **Exhausted** | **Slow** | **Average** | **Strong** | **Unstoppable**

WEEK 18 Inspiration: STEVE REDGRAVE

World rowing champion and six-time Olympic medalist

MONDAY DATE

VITAL STATS: Hometown: Marlow Bottom, Buckinghamshire, England Born: March 23,1962 Height: 6 ft 5 in / 196 cm Weight: 231 lb / 105 kg

GOAL FOR THE DAY

RESISTANCE TRAINING

Muscle Group	Exercise	Warm-Up	Set 1	Set 2	Set 3	Cooldown	Comments

CARDIO ACTIVITY

Type of Exercise	Warm-Up Period	Sustained Heart Rate	Workout Period In Sustained Heart Rate	Cooldown Period

DIET

Day's Calories	Carbohydrates	Protein	Weight

SUCCESS/DISAPPOINTMENT OF THE DAY

Overall Grade: **A** | **B** | **C** | **D** | **F** How I felt today: **Exhausted** | **Slow** | **Average** | **Strong** | **Unstoppable**

British rower **STEVE REDGRAVE** is truly sports royalty. Redgrave was knighted by Queen Elizabeth and "Sir Steve" considers that a crowning achievement in a remarkable life. Britain's most successful Olympian—five gold medals, back to back—Redgrave faced his most difficult race at the 2000 games after being diagnosed as a diabetic. Working closely with his doctor, and getting approval from Olympic officials to inject insulin, Redgrave rose above his ailment to stride, with his teammate, onto the victor's platform.

TUESDAY	DATE

GOAL FOR THE DAY

RESISTANCE TRAINING

Muscle Group	Exercise	Warm-Up	Set 1	Set 2	Set 3	Cooldown	Comments

CARDIO ACTIVITY

Type of Exercise	Warm-Up Period	Sustained Heart Rate	Workout Period In Sustained Heart Rate	Cooldown Period

DIET

Day's Calories	Carbohydrates	Protein	Weight

STRENGTH

SUCCESS/DISAPPOINTMENT OF THE DAY

Overall Grade: **A** | **B** | **C** | **D** | **F** How I felt today: **Exhausted** | **Slow** | **Average** | **Strong** | **Unstoppable**

REDGRAVE ON
MOTIVATION

WEDNESDAY | DATE

"I don't really look at it as winning a fifth gold. I'm looking to win a gold I haven't got."

GOAL FOR THE DAY

RESISTANCE TRAINING

Muscle Group	Exercise	Warm-Up	Set 1	Set 2	Set 3	Cooldown	Comments

CARDIO ACTIVITY

Type of Exercise	Warm-Up Period	Sustained Heart Rate	Workout Period In Sustained Heart Rate	Cooldown Period

DIET

Day's Calories	Carbohydrates	Protein	Weight

SUCCESS/DISAPPOINTMENT OF THE DAY

Overall Grade: **A** | **B** | **C** | **D** | **F** How I felt today: **Exhausted** | **Slow** | **Average** | **Strong** | **Unstoppable**

REDGRAVE ON PUSHING YOURSELF

THURSDAY	DATE

"There's still a lot of pressure on us because there's a lot of pressure from ourselves to do well. We know how well we can perform and we have got to try and make sure that we perform to the level that we want to, to get the results that we want to."

GOAL FOR THE DAY

RESISTANCE TRAINING

Muscle Group	Exercise	Warm-Up	Set 1	Set 2	Set 3	Cooldown	Comments

18

CARDIO ACTIVITY

Type of Exercise	Warm-Up Period	Sustained Heart Rate	Workout Period In Sustained Heart Rate	Cooldown Period

DIET

Day's Calories	Carbohydrates	Protein	Weight

SUCCESS/DISAPPOINTMENT OF THE DAY

FOCUS

Overall Grade: **A** | **B** | **C** | **D** | **F** How I felt today: **Exhausted** | **Slow** | **Average** | **Strong** | **Unstoppable**

FRIDAY | DATE

"The biggest problem we have is complacency, and always has been."

GOAL FOR THE DAY

Muscle Group	Exercise	Warm-Up	Set 1	Set 2	Set 3	Cooldown	Comments

RESISTANCE TRAINING

Type of Exercise	Warm-Up Period	Sustained Heart Rate	Workout Period In Sustained Heart Rate	Cooldown Period

CARDIO ACTIVITY

Day's Calories	Carbohydrates	Protein	Weight

DIET

SUCCESS/DISAPPOINTMENT OF THE DAY

Overall Grade: **A** | **B** | **C** | **D** | **F** How I felt today: **Exhausted** | **Slow** | **Average** | **Strong** | **Unstoppable**

SATURDAY DATE

"There's no secret to why the British team has been so successful. There's been a lot of hard work and professionalism."

GOAL FOR THE DAY

RESISTANCE TRAINING

Muscle Group	Exercise	Warm-Up	Set 1	Set 2	Set 3	Cooldown	Comments

18

CARDIO ACTIVITY

Type of Exercise	Warm-Up Period	Sustained Heart Rate	Workout Period In Sustained Heart Rate	Cooldown Period

DIET

Day's Calories	Carbohydrates	Protein	Weight

SUCCESS/DISAPPOINTMENT OF THE DAY

CHALLENGE

Overall Grade: **A** | **B** | **C** | **D** | **F** How I felt today: **Exhausted** | **Slow** | **Average** | **Strong** | **Unstoppable**

REDGRAVE ON
BREAKING THROUGH THE WALL

SUNDAY	DATE

"I feel knackered all the time. I have no energy and I'm fighting the margins of being ill and not being ill. I go to dinners and fall asleep. I'm pushing back the boundaries all the time, and training so hard it takes a toll on the body. If you feel fit and strong there's something wrong. You're not training hard enough."

GOAL FOR THE DAY

RESISTANCE TRAINING

Muscle Group	Exercise	Warm-Up	Set 1	Set 2	Set 3	Cooldown	Comments

CARDIO ACTIVITY

Type of Exercise	Warm-Up Period	Sustained Heart Rate	Workout Period In Sustained Heart Rate	Cooldown Period

DIET

Day's Calories	Carbohydrates	Protein	Weight

SUCCESS/DISAPPOINTMENT OF THE DAY

Overall Grade: **A** | **B** | **C** | **D** | **F**   How I felt today: **Exhausted** | **Slow** | **Average** | **Strong** | **Unstoppable**

WEEK 19 Inspiration: BETHANY HAMILTON

Inspirational surfer who overcame losing an arm in a shark attack

MONDAY	DATE

VITAL STATS: Hometown: Lihue, Hawaii
Born: February 8, 1990
Height : 5 ft 11 in / 180 cm Weight: 141 lb / 64 kg

GOAL FOR THE DAY

RESISTANCE TRAINING

Muscle Group	Exercise	Warm-Up	Set 1	Set 2	Set 3	Cooldown	Comments

CARDIO ACTIVITY

Type of Exercise	Warm-Up Period	Sustained Heart Rate	Workout Period In Sustained Heart Rate	Cooldown Period

DIET

Day's Calories	Carbohydrates	Protein	Weight

SUCCESS/DISAPPOINTMENT OF THE DAY

PERSEVERE

Overall Grade: **A** | **B** | **C** | **D** | **F** How I felt today: **Exhausted** | **Slow** | **Average** | **Strong** | **Unstoppable**

TUESDAY	DATE

At the age of thirteen, while out surfing, **BETHANY HAMILTON**, a rising surf star was attacked by a 14-foot tiger shark, losing her left arm just below the shoulder and 60 percent of her blood. Incredibly, Hamilton returned to surfing less than a month later. In just over a year she won her first National title and in 2007, four years after the attack, realized her dream of turning professional. She is an inspirational athlete and the epitome of determination, courage, and fighting against the odds.

GOAL FOR THE DAY

19

RESISTANCE TRAINING

Muscle Group	Exercise	Warm-Up	Set 1	Set 2	Set 3	Cooldown	Comments

CARDIO ACTIVITY

Type of Exercise	Warm-Up Period	Sustained Heart Rate	Workout Period In Sustained Heart Rate	Cooldown Period

DIET

Day's Calories	Carbohydrates	Protein	Weight

SUCCESS/DISAPPOINTMENT OF THE DAY

Overall Grade: **A** | **B** | **C** | **D** | **F** How I felt today: **Exhausted** | **Slow** | **Average** | **Strong** | **Unstoppable**

HAMILTON ON
COURAGE

WEDNESDAY | DATE

"Courage doesn't mean you don't get afraid. Courage means you don't let fear stop you."

GOAL FOR THE DAY

RESISTANCE TRAINING

Muscle Group	Exercise	Warm-Up	Set 1	Set 2	Set 3	Cooldown	Comments

CARDIO ACTIVITY

Type of Exercise	Warm-Up Period	Sustained Heart Rate	Workout Period In Sustained Heart Rate	Cooldown Period

DIET

Day's Calories	Carbohydrates	Protein	Weight

SACRIFICE

SUCCESS/DISAPPOINTMENT OF THE DAY

Overall Grade: **A** | **B** | **C** | **D** | **F**   How I felt today: **Exhausted** | **Slow** | **Average** | **Strong** | **Unstoppable**

HAMILTON ON
PUSHING BOUNDARIES

THURSDAY	DATE

"I don't want easy, just possible."

GOAL FOR THE DAY

RESISTANCE TRAINING

Muscle Group	Exercise	Warm-Up	Set 1	Set 2	Set 3	Cooldown	Comments

19

CARDIO ACTIVITY

Type of Exercise	Warm-Up Period	Sustained Heart Rate	Workout Period In Sustained Heart Rate	Cooldown Period

DIET

Day's Calories	Carbohydrates	Protein	Weight

SUCCESS/DISAPPOINTMENT OF THE DAY

Overall Grade: **A** | **B** | **C** | **D** | **F**   How I felt today: **Exhausted** | **Slow** | **Average** | **Strong** | **Unstoppable**

HAMILTON ON OVERCOMING DOUBT

FRIDAY	DATE

"It's hard for me to describe the joy I felt after I stood up and rode a wave for the first time after the attack. I was incredibly thankful and happy inside. The tiny bit of doubt that would sometimes tell me you'll never surf again was gone in one wave."

GOAL FOR THE DAY

RESISTANCE TRAINING

Muscle Group	Exercise	Warm-Up	Set 1	Set 2	Set 3	Cooldown	Comments

19

CARDIO ACTIVITY

Type of Exercise	Warm-Up Period	Sustained Heart Rate	Workout Period In Sustained Heart Rate	Cooldown Period

DIET

Day's Calories	Carbohydrates	Protein	Weight

SUCCESS/DISAPPOINTMENT OF THE DAY

BREAK THROUGH

Overall Grade: **A** | **B** | **C** | **D** | **F**   How I felt today: **Exhausted** | **Slow** | **Average** | **Strong** | **Unstoppable**

HAMILTON ON
TRAINING

SATURDAY	DATE

"Besides surfing, I play tennis, volleyball, I swim, I run hills, or I do high-intensity, high-interval workouts. I'm up at 5 A.M. every day."

GOAL FOR THE DAY

RESISTANCE TRAINING

Muscle Group	Exercise	Warm-Up	Set 1	Set 2	Set 3	Cooldown	Comments

CARDIO ACTIVITY

Type of Exercise	Warm-Up Period	Sustained Heart Rate	Workout Period In Sustained Heart Rate	Cooldown Period

DIET

Day's Calories	Carbohydrates	Protein	Weight

SUCCESS/DISAPPOINTMENT OF THE DAY

Overall Grade: **A** | **B** | **C** | **D** | **F** How I felt today: **Exhausted** | **Slow** | **Average** | **Strong** | **Unstoppable**

HAMILTON ON HAVING FUN

SUNDAY	DATE

"I think it doesn't matter if you are the best surfer in the world. I'm going to try to be the best surfer I can be. It's not all about competing and being the best. It's more about having fun and just doing what you love."

GOAL FOR THE DAY

RESISTANCE TRAINING

Muscle Group	Exercise	Warm-Up	Set 1	Set 2	Set 3	Cooldown	Comments

CARDIO ACTIVITY

Type of Exercise	Warm-Up Period	Sustained Heart Rate	Workout Period In Sustained Heart Rate	Cooldown Period

DIET

Day's Calories	Carbohydrates	Protein	Weight

ACHIEVE

SUCCESS/DISAPPOINTMENT OF THE DAY

Overall Grade: **A** | **B** | **C** | **D** | **F** How I felt today: **Exhausted** | **Slow** | **Average** | **Strong** | **Unstoppable**

WEEK 20 Inspiration: EMMITT SMITH

All-time American football leader in rushing yards and touchdowns

MONDAY	DATE

VITAL STATS: Hometown: Pensacola, Florida
Born: May 15, 1969
Height: 5 ft 10 in / 178 cm Weight: 209 lb / 95 kg

GOAL FOR THE DAY

RESISTANCE TRAINING

Muscle Group	Exercise	Warm-Up	Set 1	Set 2	Set 3	Cooldown	Comments

CARDIO ACTIVITY

Type of Exercise	Warm-Up Period	Sustained Heart Rate	Workout Period In Sustained Heart Rate	Cooldown Period

DIET

Day's Calories	Carbohydrates	Protein	Weight

SUCCESS/DISAPPOINTMENT OF THE DAY

Overall Grade: **A** | **B** | **C** | **D** | **F**   How I felt today: **Exhausted** | **Slow** | **Average** | **Strong** | **Unstoppable**

Former American football running back, **EMMITT SMITH** prides himself on being a pace-setter on and off the field. His trophy case is packed with MVP awards, Super Bowl memorabilia, and Pro Bowl mementoes. Not a physically tall man, the football star packed his medium-height frame with muscle. After leaving college early in 1990, Emmitt promised his mother he would earn a B.A. He added a college diploma to his football accolades in 1996, grabbing that graduation goal.

TUESDAY	DATE

GOAL FOR THE DAY

RESISTANCE TRAINING

Muscle Group	Exercise	Warm-Up	Set 1	Set 2	Set 3	Cooldown	Comments

20

CARDIO ACTIVITY

Type of Exercise	Warm-Up Period	Sustained Heart Rate	Workout Period In Sustained Heart Rate	Cooldown Period

DIET

Day's Calories	Carbohydrates	Protein	Weight

SUCCESS/DISAPPOINTMENT OF THE DAY

SUCCESS

Overall Grade: **A** | **B** | **C** | **D** | **F**   How I felt today: **Exhausted** | **Slow** | **Average** | **Strong** | **Unstoppable**

SMITH ON
WINNING

WEDNESDAY | DATE

"For me, winning isn't something that happens suddenly on the field when the whistle blows and the crowds roar. Winning is something that builds physically and mentally every day that you train and every night that you dream."

GOAL FOR THE DAY

RESISTANCE TRAINING

Muscle Group	Exercise	Warm-Up	Set 1	Set 2	Set 3	Cooldown	Comments

CARDIO ACTIVITY

Type of Exercise	Warm-Up Period	Sustained Heart Rate	Workout Period In Sustained Heart Rate	Cooldown Period

DIET

Day's Calories	Carbohydrates	Protein	Weight

SUCCESS/DISAPPOINTMENT OF THE DAY

Overall Grade: **A** | **B** | **C** | **D** | **F**   How I felt today: **Exhausted** | **Slow** | **Average** | **Strong** | **Unstoppable**

SMITH ON PERSPECTIVE

THURSDAY | DATE

"I might win, I might lose, but I will never be defeated."

GOAL FOR THE DAY

RESISTANCE TRAINING

Muscle Group	Exercise	Warm-Up	Set 1	Set 2	Set 3	Cooldown	Comments

CARDIO ACTIVITY

Type of Exercise	Warm-Up Period	Sustained Heart Rate	Workout Period In Sustained Heart Rate	Cooldown Period

DIET

Day's Calories	Carbohydrates	Protein	Weight

FINISH IT

SUCCESS/DISAPPOINTMENT OF THE DAY

Overall Grade: **A** | **B** | **C** | **D** | **F**   How I felt today: **Exhausted** | **Slow** | **Average** | **Strong** | **Unstoppable**

SMITH ON
STRIVING TO BE A LEGEND

FRIDAY	DATE

"I think of being the greatest. I think about it all the time. I'm chasing after legends, after Walter Payton and Tony Dorsett and Jim Brown and Eric Dickerson, after guys who made history. When my career's over, I want to have the new kids, the new backs, say, "Boy, we have to chase a legend to be the best." And they'll mean Emmitt Smith."

GOAL FOR THE DAY

RESISTANCE TRAINING

Muscle Group	Exercise	Warm-Up	Set 1	Set 2	Set 3	Cooldown	Comments

CARDIO ACTIVITY

Type of Exercise	Warm-Up Period	Sustained Heart Rate	Workout Period In Sustained Heart Rate	Cooldown Period

DIET

Day's Calories	Carbohydrates	Protein	Weight

SUCCESS/DISAPPOINTMENT OF THE DAY

Overall Grade: **A** | **B** | **C** | **D** | **F**   How I felt today: **Exhausted** | **Slow** | **Average** | **Strong** | **Unstoppable**

SMITH ON DRIVE

SATURDAY | DATE

"If you're satisfied, you're finished. You can never be satisfied."

GOAL FOR THE DAY

RESISTANCE TRAINING

Muscle Group	Exercise	Warm-Up	Set 1	Set 2	Set 3	Cooldown	Comments

CARDIO ACTIVITY

Type of Exercise	Warm-Up Period	Sustained Heart Rate	Workout Period In Sustained Heart Rate	Cooldown Period

DIET

Day's Calories	Carbohydrates	Protein	Weight

WIN

SUCCESS/DISAPPOINTMENT OF THE DAY

Overall Grade: **A** | **B** | **C** | **D** | **F** How I felt today: **Exhausted** | **Slow** | **Average** | **Strong** | **Unstoppable**

SMITH ON LEADERSHIP

SUNDAY | DATE

"My job is to play football the best way I know how, to practice and work as hard as I know how, and to lead by example and help out whenever I can. I have to have a positive attitude about it, and I've got to encourage other people because they look to me for leadership. You can't be a leader if you're going to mope around and complain."

GOAL FOR THE DAY

RESISTANCE TRAINING

Muscle Group	Exercise	Warm-Up	Set 1	Set 2	Set 3	Cooldown	Comments

CARDIO ACTIVITY

Type of Exercise	Warm-Up Period	Sustained Heart Rate	Workout Period In Sustained Heart Rate	Cooldown Period

DIET

Day's Calories	Carbohydrates	Protein	Weight

SUCCESS/DISAPPOINTMENT OF THE DAY

Overall Grade: **A** | **B** | **C** | **D** | **F**   How I felt today: **Exhausted** | **Slow** | **Average** | **Strong** | **Unstoppable**

WEEK 21 Inspiration: NAIM SULEYMANOGLU

World champion weight lifter and three-time Olympic medalist

MONDAY	DATE

VITAL STATS: Hometown: Ptichar, Bulgaria
Born: January 23,1967
Height: 4 ft 11 in / 150 cm Weight: 141 lb / 64 kg

GOAL FOR THE DAY

RESISTANCE TRAINING

Muscle Group	Exercise	Warm-Up	Set 1	Set 2	Set 3	Cooldown	Comments

CARDIO ACTIVITY

Type of Exercise	Warm-Up Period	Sustained Heart Rate	Workout Period In Sustained Heart Rate	Cooldown Period

DIET

Day's Calories	Carbohydrates	Protein	Weight

EXCEL

SUCCESS/DISAPPOINTMENT OF THE DAY

Overall Grade: **A** | **B** | **C** | **D** | **F** How I felt today: **Exhausted** | **Slow** | **Average** | **Strong** | **Unstoppable**

NAIM SULEYMANOGLU picked up his first weights at age ten and set a world record by sixteen. But he missed his chance to snatch Olympic gold in 1984 when Bulgaria joined the Soviet boycott. While competing at the 1986 World Championship, he fled his homeland. His winning a gold medal at the 1988 Olympics was assured—so much so that Bulgaria charged Turkey $us 1 million to have "Pocket Hercules" lift for their national pride. By the time he retired in 2000, Suleymanoglu had collected three Olympic golds, and bested forty-six world records.

TUESDAY	DATE

GOAL FOR THE DAY

RESISTANCE TRAINING

Muscle Group	Exercise	Warm-Up	Set 1	Set 2	Set 3	Cooldown	Comments

CARDIO ACTIVITY

Type of Exercise	Warm-Up Period	Sustained Heart Rate	Workout Period In Sustained Heart Rate	Cooldown Period

DIET

Day's Calories	Carbohydrates	Protein	Weight

SUCCESS/DISAPPOINTMENT OF THE DAY

Overall Grade: **A** | **B** | **C** | **D** | **F**   How I felt today: **Exhausted** | **Slow** | **Average** | **Strong** | **Unstoppable**

SULEYMANOGLU ON
CHALLENGING YOURSELF

WEDNESDAY	DATE

"I should be satisfied! But a sportsman can never be satisfied."

GOAL FOR THE DAY

RESISTANCE TRAINING

Muscle Group	Exercise	Warm-Up	Set 1	Set 2	Set 3	Cooldown	Comments

CARDIO ACTIVITY

Type of Exercise	Warm-Up Period	Sustained Heart Rate	Workout Period In Sustained Heart Rate	Cooldown Period

DIET

Day's Calories	Carbohydrates	Protein	Weight

FIGHT

SUCCESS/DISAPPOINTMENT OF THE DAY

Overall Grade: **A** | **B** | **C** | **D** | **F** How I felt today: **Exhausted** | **Slow** | **Average** | **Strong** | **Unstoppable**

SULEYMANOGLU ON SUCCESS AT ANY AGE

THURSDAY | DATE

"Being young is not enough, nor is it absolutely necessary. Just never lose your motivation and steadfastness and you will get along."

GOAL FOR THE DAY

RESISTANCE TRAINING

Muscle Group	Exercise	Warm-Up	Set 1	Set 2	Set 3	Cooldown	Comments

CARDIO ACTIVITY

Type of Exercise	Warm-Up Period	Sustained Heart Rate	Workout Period In Sustained Heart Rate	Cooldown Period

DIET

Day's Calories	Carbohydrates	Protein	Weight

SUCCESS/DISAPPOINTMENT OF THE DAY

Overall Grade: **A** | **B** | **C** | **D** | **F**   How I felt today: **Exhausted** | **Slow** | **Average** | **Strong** | **Unstoppable**

SULEYMANOGLU ON
AIMING HIGH

FRIDAY	DATE

"I know only gold. I do not know about silver or bronze."

GOAL FOR THE DAY

RESISTANCE TRAINING

Muscle Group	Exercise	Warm-Up	Set 1	Set 2	Set 3	Cooldown	Comments

CARDIO ACTIVITY

Type of Exercise	Warm-Up Period	Sustained Heart Rate	Workout Period In Sustained Heart Rate	Cooldown Period

DIET

Day's Calories	Carbohydrates	Protein	Weight

STRENGTH

SUCCESS/DISAPPOINTMENT OF THE DAY

Overall Grade: **A** | **B** | **C** | **D** | **F** How I felt today: **Exhausted** | **Slow** | **Average** | **Strong** | **Unstoppable**

SULEYMANOGLU ON
INSPIRATION

SATURDAY	DATE

"I get my strength from the 55 million Turks who believe in me."

GOAL FOR THE DAY

RESISTANCE TRAINING

Muscle Group	Exercise	Warm-Up	Set 1	Set 2	Set 3	Cooldown	Comments

CARDIO ACTIVITY

Type of Exercise	Warm-Up Period	Sustained Heart Rate	Workout Period In Sustained Heart Rate	Cooldown Period

DIET

Day's Calories	Carbohydrates	Protein	Weight

SUCCESS/DISAPPOINTMENT OF THE DAY

Overall Grade: **A** | **B** | **C** | **D** | **F** How I felt today: **Exhausted** | **Slow** | **Average** | **Strong** | **Unstoppable**

SULEYMANOGLU ON COMPETITION

SUNDAY | DATE

"I have lifted 195 [kg] in training. But in practice or warm-up it counts for nothing. You must go to the podium and do it there."

GOAL FOR THE DAY

RESISTANCE TRAINING

Muscle Group	Exercise	Warm-Up	Set 1	Set 2	Set 3	Cooldown	Comments

CARDIO ACTIVITY

Type of Exercise	Warm-Up Period	Sustained Heart Rate	Workout Period In Sustained Heart Rate	Cooldown Period

DIET

Day's Calories	Carbohydrates	Protein	Weight

SUCCESS/DISAPPOINTMENT OF THE DAY

FOCUS

Overall Grade: **A** | **B** | **C** | **D** | **F** How I felt today: **Exhausted** | **Slow** | **Average** | **Strong** | **Unstoppable**

WEEK 22 Inspiration: IAN THORPE

Five-time Olympic medalist and world-record-breaking swimmer

MONDAY | DATE

VITAL STATS: Hometown: Sydney, Australia
Born: October 13, 1982
Height: 6 ft 5 in / 196 cm Weight: 200 lb / 91 kg

GOAL FOR THE DAY

RESISTANCE TRAINING

Muscle Group	Exercise	Warm-Up	Set 1	Set 2	Set 3	Cooldown	Comments

CARDIO ACTIVITY

Type of Exercise	Warm-Up Period	Sustained Heart Rate	Workout Period In Sustained Heart Rate	Cooldown Period

DIET

Day's Calories	Carbohydrates	Protein	Weight

SUCCESS/DISAPPOINTMENT OF THE DAY

Overall Grade: **A** | **B** | **C** | **D** | **F** How I felt today: **Exhausted** | **Slow** | **Average** | **Strong** | **Unstoppable**

Allergic to chlorine, **IAN THORPE** was a dedicated landlubber. Then one day he recklessly jumped into a pool. His older sister was a junior competitor, and he wanted to see how he would compare. While awkwardly holding his face out of the water, he exhibited an unusual and unbeatable gait. His new identity was forged: Thorpedo. Ian strived for one goal: to best his last best. He has achieved it, breaking more than twenty world records.

TUESDAY	DATE

GOAL FOR THE DAY

RESISTANCE TRAINING

Muscle Group	Exercise	Warm-Up	Set 1	Set 2	Set 3	Cooldown	Comments

CARDIO ACTIVITY

Type of Exercise	Warm-Up Period	Sustained Heart Rate	Workout Period In Sustained Heart Rate	Cooldown Period

DIET

Day's Calories	Carbohydrates	Protein	Weight

SUCCESS/DISAPPOINTMENT OF THE DAY

CHALLENGE

Overall Grade: **A** | **B** | **C** | **D** | **F** How I felt today: **Exhausted** | **Slow** | **Average** | **Strong** | **Unstoppable**

THORPE ON
PUSHING HIMSELF

WEDNESDAY	DATE

"My expectations are far greater than anyone can put on me. I do all the hard work; I know what I want from myself and what I expect from myself. When it comes to expectation, I'm my hardest critic."

GOAL FOR THE DAY

RESISTANCE TRAINING

Muscle Group	Exercise	Warm-Up	Set 1	Set 2	Set 3	Cooldown	Comments

CARDIO ACTIVITY

Type of Exercise	Warm-Up Period	Sustained Heart Rate	Workout Period In Sustained Heart Rate	Cooldown Period

DIET

Day's Calories	Carbohydrates	Protein	Weight

SUCCESS/DISAPPOINTMENT OF THE DAY

Overall Grade: **A** | **B** | **C** | **D** | **F** How I felt today: **Exhausted** | **Slow** | **Average** | **Strong** | **Unstoppable**

THORPE ON
THE PRESSURE OF EXPECTATIONS

THURSDAY | DATE

"[They're not] weighing me down, but a weight pushing behind me."

GOAL FOR THE DAY

RESISTANCE TRAINING

Muscle Group	Exercise	Warm-Up	Set 1	Set 2	Set 3	Cooldown	Comments

CARDIO ACTIVITY

Type of Exercise	Warm-Up Period	Sustained Heart Rate	Workout Period In Sustained Heart Rate	Cooldown Period

DIET

Day's Calories	Carbohydrates	Protein	Weight

PERSEVERE

SUCCESS/DISAPPOINTMENT OF THE DAY

Overall Grade: **A** | **B** | **C** | **D** | **F** How I felt today: **Exhausted** | **Slow** | **Average** | **Strong** | **Unstoppable**

THORPE ON MOTIVATION

FRIDAY	DATE

"I always just try to swim personal bests and if that means breaking world records then so be it. My goal now is to swim a personal best at every major meet."

GOAL FOR THE DAY

RESISTANCE TRAINING

Muscle Group	Exercise	Warm-Up	Set 1	Set 2	Set 3	Cooldown	Comments

22

CARDIO ACTIVITY

Type of Exercise	Warm-Up Period	Sustained Heart Rate	Workout Period In Sustained Heart Rate	Cooldown Period

DIET

Day's Calories	Carbohydrates	Protein	Weight

SUCCESS/DISAPPOINTMENT OF THE DAY

Overall Grade: **A** | **B** | **C** | **D** | **F** How I felt today: **Exhausted** | **Slow** | **Average** | **Strong** | **Unstoppable**

THORPE ON DETERMINATION

SATURDAY | DATE

"I'm determined to get the best out of myself. That's why I get up at four every morning. That's why I train and train. I really love what I do, and that's why I do it."

GOAL FOR THE DAY

RESISTANCE TRAINING

Muscle Group	Exercise	Warm-Up	Set 1	Set 2	Set 3	Cooldown	Comments

CARDIO ACTIVITY

Type of Exercise	Warm-Up Period	Sustained Heart Rate	Workout Period In Sustained Heart Rate	Cooldown Period

DIET

Day's Calories	Carbohydrates	Protein	Weight

SACRIFICE

SUCCESS/DISAPPOINTMENT OF THE DAY

Overall Grade: **A** | **B** | **C** | **D** | **F** How I felt today: **Exhausted** | **Slow** | **Average** | **Strong** | **Unstoppable**

THORPE ON
ACHIEVEMENT

SUNDAY | DATE

"I don't need a motivator. I'm motivated enough."

GOAL FOR THE DAY

RESISTANCE TRAINING

Muscle Group	Exercise	Warm-Up	Set 1	Set 2	Set 3	Cooldown	Comments

CARDIO ACTIVITY

Type of Exercise	Warm-Up Period	Sustained Heart Rate	Workout Period In Sustained Heart Rate	Cooldown Period

DIET

Day's Calories	Carbohydrates	Protein	Weight

SUCCESS/DISAPPOINTMENT OF THE DAY

Overall Grade: **A** | **B** | **C** | **D** | **F** How I felt today: **Exhausted** | **Slow** | **Average** | **Strong** | **Unstoppable**

WEEK 23 Inspiration: LEBRON JAMES

Two-time NBA Champion and eleven-time NBA All-Star

MONDAY	DATE

VITAL STATS: Hometown: Akron, Ohio
Born: December 30, 1984
Height: 6 ft 8 in / 203 cm Weight: 250 lb / 80 kg

GOAL FOR THE DAY

RESISTANCE TRAINING

Muscle Group	Exercise	Warm-Up	Set 1	Set 2	Set 3	Cooldown	Comments

CARDIO ACTIVITY

Type of Exercise	Warm-Up Period	Sustained Heart Rate	Workout Period In Sustained Heart Rate	Cooldown Period

DIET

Day's Calories	Carbohydrates	Protein	Weight

SUCCESS/DISAPPOINTMENT OF THE DAY

BREAK THROUGH

Overall Grade: **A** | **B** | **C** | **D** | **F** How I felt today: **Exhausted** | **Slow** | **Average** | **Strong** | **Unstoppable**

LEBRON JAMES is a superstar of the NBA. Four MVP awards in five years (matched only by Bill Russell) suggest James is not a normal player. He is exceptionally talented and athletic but more so has great versatility, with exceptional career averages for points, rebounds and assists, and an ability to continuously work on and improve his game. He is the highest paid player in the NBA and a global icon. He continues to perform heroics for the Cleveland Cavaliers under the greatest of spotlights.

TUESDAY	DATE

GOAL FOR THE DAY

RESISTANCE TRAINING

Muscle Group	Exercise	Warm-Up	Set 1	Set 2	Set 3	Cooldown	Comments

CARDIO ACTIVITY

Type of Exercise	Warm-Up Period	Sustained Heart Rate	Workout Period In Sustained Heart Rate	Cooldown Period

DIET

Day's Calories	Carbohydrates	Protein	Weight

SUCCESS/DISAPPOINTMENT OF THE DAY

Overall Grade: **A** | **B** | **C** | **D** | **F** How I felt today: **Exhausted** | **Slow** | **Average** | **Strong** | **Unstoppable**

JAMES ON FEAR

WEDNESDAY | DATE

"You can't be afraid to fail. It's the only way you succeed—you're not gonna succeed all the time, and I know that."

GOAL FOR THE DAY

RESISTANCE TRAINING

Muscle Group	Exercise	Warm-Up	Set 1	Set 2	Set 3	Cooldown	Comments

CARDIO ACTIVITY

Type of Exercise	Warm-Up Period	Sustained Heart Rate	Workout Period In Sustained Heart Rate	Cooldown Period

DIET

Day's Calories	Carbohydrates	Protein	Weight

SUCCESS/DISAPPOINTMENT OF THE DAY

ACHIEVE

Overall Grade: **A** | **B** | **C** | **D** | **F** How I felt today: **Exhausted** | **Slow** | **Average** | **Strong** | **Unstoppable**

JAMES ON CRITICISM

THURSDAY	DATE

"I like criticism. It makes you strong."

GOAL FOR THE DAY

Muscle Group	Exercise	Warm-Up	Set 1	Set 2	Set 3	Cooldown	Comments

RESISTANCE TRAINING

Type of Exercise	Warm-Up Period	Sustained Heart Rate	Workout Period In Sustained Heart Rate	Cooldown Period

CARDIO ACTIVITY

Day's Calories	Carbohydrates	Protein	Weight

DIET

SUCCESS/DISAPPOINTMENT OF THE DAY

Overall Grade: **A** | **B** | **C** | **D** | **F** How I felt today: **Exhausted** | **Slow** | **Average** | **Strong** | **Unstoppable**

JAMES ON GIVING HIS ALL

FRIDAY | DATE

"Every night on the court I give my all, and if I'm not giving 100 percent, I criticize myself."

GOAL FOR THE DAY

RESISTANCE TRAINING

Muscle Group	Exercise	Warm-Up	Set 1	Set 2	Set 3	Cooldown	Comments

CARDIO ACTIVITY

Type of Exercise	Warm-Up Period	Sustained Heart Rate	Workout Period In Sustained Heart Rate	Cooldown Period

DIET

Day's Calories	Carbohydrates	Protein	Weight

SUCCESS

SUCCESS/DISAPPOINTMENT OF THE DAY

Overall Grade: **A** | **B** | **C** | **D** | **F** How I felt today: **Exhausted** | **Slow** | **Average** | **Strong** | **Unstoppable**

JAMES ON
BEING THE BEST

SATURDAY | DATE

"Everywhere I've been, I've been the best player. I love being a leader, and I love being the best. I just want to get better. It's not about being cocky or selfish or anything like that. It's just how I am."

GOAL FOR THE DAY

RESISTANCE TRAINING

Muscle Group	Exercise	Warm-Up	Set 1	Set 2	Set 3	Cooldown	Comments

CARDIO ACTIVITY

Type of Exercise	Warm-Up Period	Sustained Heart Rate	Workout Period In Sustained Heart Rate	Cooldown Period

DIET

Day's Calories	Carbohydrates	Protein	Weight

SUCCESS/DISAPPOINTMENT OF THE DAY

Overall Grade: **A** | **B** | **C** | **D** | **F** How I felt today: **Exhausted** | **Slow** | **Average** | **Strong** | **Unstoppable**

JAMES ON
PRESSURE

SUNDAY	DATE

"I hear that word pressure all the time. There is a lot of pressure put on me, but I don't put a lot of pressure on myself. I feel if I play my game, it will take care of itself."

GOAL FOR THE DAY

RESISTANCE TRAINING

Muscle Group	Exercise	Warm-Up	Set 1	Set 2	Set 3	Cooldown	Comments

CARDIO ACTIVITY

Type of Exercise	Warm-Up Period	Sustained Heart Rate	Workout Period In Sustained Heart Rate	Cooldown Period

DIET

Day's Calories	Carbohydrates	Protein	Weight

SUCCESS/DISAPPOINTMENT OF THE DAY

FINISH IT

Overall Grade: **A** | **B** | **C** | **D** | **F** How I felt today: **Exhausted** | **Slow** | **Average** | **Strong** | **Unstoppable**

WEEK 24 Inspiration: GABBY DOUGLAS

Individual all-around and team Olympic champion

MONDAY	DATE

VITAL STATS: Hometown: Newport News, Virginia
Born: December 31, 1995
Height: 4 ft 11 in / 150 cm Weight: 90 lb / 41 kg

GOAL FOR THE DAY

RESISTANCE TRAINING

Muscle Group	Exercise	Warm-Up	Set 1	Set 2	Set 3	Cooldown	Comments

CARDIO ACTIVITY

Type of Exercise	Warm-Up Period	Sustained Heart Rate	Workout Period In Sustained Heart Rate	Cooldown Period

DIET

Day's Calories	Carbohydrates	Protein	Weight

SUCCESS/DISAPPOINTMENT OF THE DAY

Overall Grade: **A** | **B** | **C** | **D** | **F** How I felt today: **Exhausted** | **Slow** | **Average** | **Strong** | **Unstoppable**

Having been introduced to gymnastics by her sister as a toddler, **GABBY DOUGLAS** did not begin formal training until the age of seven, yet within two years was State Champion. At forteen Douglas moved away from home to train with Liang Chow. This move precipitated an incredible trajectory over the next two years. In 2010 Douglas placed fourth all-around at the U.S. Junior National Championships, and by the end of 2012 she was a World and Olympic team champion and all-around gold medalist at the London Olympics.

TUESDAY DATE

GOAL FOR THE DAY

24

RESISTANCE TRAINING

Muscle Group	Exercise	Warm-Up	Set 1	Set 2	Set 3	Cooldown	Comments

CARDIO ACTIVITY

Type of Exercise	Warm-Up Period	Sustained Heart Rate	Workout Period In Sustained Heart Rate	Cooldown Period

DIET

Day's Calories	Carbohydrates	Protein	Weight

SUCCESS/DISAPPOINTMENT OF THE DAY

WIN

Overall Grade: **A** | **B** | **C** | **D** | **F** How I felt today: **Exhausted** | **Slow** | **Average** | **Strong** | **Unstoppable**

WEDNESDAY	DATE

"Gold medals are made out of sweat, blood and tears and effort in the gym every day."

GOAL FOR THE DAY

RESISTANCE TRAINING

Muscle Group	Exercise	Warm-Up	Set 1	Set 2	Set 3	Cooldown	Comments

CARDIO ACTIVITY

Type of Exercise	Warm-Up Period	Sustained Heart Rate	Workout Period In Sustained Heart Rate	Cooldown Period

DIET

Day's Calories	Carbohydrates	Protein	Weight

SUCCESS/DISAPPOINTMENT OF THE DAY

Overall Grade: **A** | **B** | **C** | **D** | **F** How I felt today: **Exhausted** | **Slow** | **Average** | **Strong** | **Unstoppable**

DOUGLAS ON
DETERMINATION

THURSDAY	DATE

"The hard days are the best because that's where champions are made so if you can push through, you can push through anything!"

GOAL FOR THE DAY

RESISTANCE TRAINING

Muscle Group	Exercise	Warm-Up	Set 1	Set 2	Set 3	Cooldown	Comments

CARDIO ACTIVITY

Type of Exercise	Warm-Up Period	Sustained Heart Rate	Workout Period In Sustained Heart Rate	Cooldown Period

DIET

Day's Calories	Carbohydrates	Protein	Weight

EXCEL

SUCCESS/DISAPPOINTMENT OF THE DAY

Overall Grade: **A** | **B** | **C** | **D** | **F** How I felt today: **Exhausted** | **Slow** | **Average** | **Strong** | **Unstoppable**

DOUGLAS ON COURAGE

FRIDAY | DATE

"You just have to be yourself and go full with confidence and be courageous."

GOAL FOR THE DAY

Muscle Group	Exercise	Warm-Up	Set 1	Set 2	Set 3	Cooldown	Comments

RESISTANCE TRAINING

Type of Exercise	Warm-Up Period	Sustained Heart Rate	Workout Period In Sustained Heart Rate	Cooldown Period

CARDIO ACTIVITY

Day's Calories	Carbohydrates	Protein	Weight

DIET

SUCCESS/DISAPPOINTMENT OF THE DAY

Overall Grade: **A** | **B** | **C** | **D** | **F** How I felt today: **Exhausted** | **Slow** | **Average** | **Strong** | **Unstoppable**

DOUGLAS ON
FACING CHALLENGES

SATURDAY | DATE

"I had to face a lot coming through this journey, a lot of sacrifices, difficulties, challenges, and injuries."

GOAL FOR THE DAY

RESISTANCE TRAINING

Muscle Group	Exercise	Warm-Up	Set 1	Set 2	Set 3	Cooldown	Comments

CARDIO ACTIVITY

Type of Exercise	Warm-Up Period	Sustained Heart Rate	Workout Period In Sustained Heart Rate	Cooldown Period

DIET

Day's Calories	Carbohydrates	Protein	Weight

FIGHT

SUCCESS/DISAPPOINTMENT OF THE DAY

Overall Grade: **A** | **B** | **C** | **D** | **F** How I felt today: **Exhausted** | **Slow** | **Average** | **Strong** | **Unstoppable**

DOUGLAS ON
BEING A SUPERHERO

SUNDAY	DATE

"I kind of do think of myself as a superhero and just flying high, and doing these crazy flips."

GOAL FOR THE DAY

RESISTANCE TRAINING

Muscle Group	Exercise	Warm-Up	Set 1	Set 2	Set 3	Cooldown	Comments

CARDIO ACTIVITY

Type of Exercise	Warm-Up Period	Sustained Heart Rate	Workout Period In Sustained Heart Rate	Cooldown Period

DIET

Day's Calories	Carbohydrates	Protein	Weight

SUCCESS/DISAPPOINTMENT OF THE DAY

Overall Grade: **A** | **B** | **C** | **D** | **F**   How I felt today: **Exhausted** | **Slow** | **Average** | **Strong** | **Unstoppable**

WEEK 25 Inspiration: YAO MING

First Chinese player in the NBA 2nd 2003 All-Star

MONDAY DATE

VITAL STATS: Hometown: Shanghai, China
Born: September 12, 1980
Height: 7 ft 6 in / 229 cm Weight: 310 lb / 141 kg

GOAL FOR THE DAY

RESISTANCE TRAINING

Muscle Group	Exercise	Warm-Up	Set 1	Set 2	Set 3	Cooldown	Comments

CARDIO ACTIVITY

Type of Exercise	Warm-Up Period	Sustained Heart Rate	Workout Period In Sustained Heart Rate	Cooldown Period

DIET

Day's Calories	Carbohydrates	Protein	Weight

SUCCESS/DISAPPOINTMENT OF THE DAY

STRENGTH

Overall Grade: **A** | **B** | **C** | **D** | **F** How I felt today: **Exhausted** | **Slow** | **Average** | **Strong** | **Unstoppable**

Born to basketball jocks, **YAO MING** seemed destined for hoops glory. Nothing could be less true. He was gangly as a youngster, and often was muscled away from the basket by stockier students. But at twelve he pledged to improve. From then on, his life shifted. Though he was a leading player for China's Shanghai Sharks, Yao Ming had to increase his skills, stamina, and stature to debut with the Houston Rockets. The fans were impressed by his emergence in the NBA, and rewarded him with All-Star honors.

TUESDAY	DATE

GOAL FOR THE DAY

RESISTANCE TRAINING

Muscle Group	Exercise	Warm-Up	Set 1	Set 2	Set 3	Cooldown	Comments

CARDIO ACTIVITY

Type of Exercise	Warm-Up Period	Sustained Heart Rate	Workout Period In Sustained Heart Rate	Cooldown Period

DIET

Day's Calories	Carbohydrates	Protein	Weight

SUCCESS/DISAPPOINTMENT OF THE DAY

Overall Grade: A | B | C | D | F

How I felt today: **Exhausted** | **Slow** | **Average** | **Strong** | **Unstoppable**

YAO ON
BREAKING THROUGH THE WALL

WEDNESDAY	DATE

"I felt very tired, to the point that I felt numb. But I had to force myself to keep going. The feeling of being tired is a bad feeling, but the feeling of losing is even worse."

GOAL FOR THE DAY

RESISTANCE TRAINING

Muscle Group	Exercise	Warm-Up	Set 1	Set 2	Set 3	Cooldown	Comments

CARDIO ACTIVITY

Type of Exercise	Warm-Up Period	Sustained Heart Rate	Workout Period In Sustained Heart Rate	Cooldown Period

DIET

Day's Calories	Carbohydrates	Protein	Weight

FOCUS

SUCCESS/DISAPPOINTMENT OF THE DAY

Overall Grade: **A** | **B** | **C** | **D** | **F** How I felt today: **Exhausted** | **Slow** | **Average** | **Strong** | **Unstoppable**

YAO ON
BEING AGGRESSIVE

THURSDAY	DATE

"I can't wait for people to attack me. I have to attack them."

GOAL FOR THE DAY

RESISTANCE TRAINING

Muscle Group	Exercise	Warm-Up	Set 1	Set 2	Set 3	Cooldown	Comments

CARDIO ACTIVITY

Type of Exercise	Warm-Up Period	Sustained Heart Rate	Workout Period In Sustained Heart Rate	Cooldown Period

DIET

Day's Calories	Carbohydrates	Protein	Weight

SUCCESS/DISAPPOINTMENT OF THE DAY

Overall Grade: **A** | **B** | **C** | **D** | **F**   How I felt today: **Exhausted** | **Slow** | **Average** | **Strong** | **Unstoppable**

YAO ON WINNING

FRIDAY	DATE

"I can only say that I don't want to lose. Every time I play, every time I go out, I don't want to lose. This is basketball. It's not soccer. There are no draws."

GOAL FOR THE DAY

RESISTANCE TRAINING

Muscle Group	Exercise	Warm-Up	Set 1	Set 2	Set 3	Cooldown	Comments

CARDIO ACTIVITY

Type of Exercise	Warm-Up Period	Sustained Heart Rate	Workout Period In Sustained Heart Rate	Cooldown Period

DIET

Day's Calories	Carbohydrates	Protein	Weight

SUCCESS/DISAPPOINTMENT OF THE DAY

CHALLENGE

Overall Grade: **A** | **B** | **C** | **D** | **F** How I felt today: **Exhausted** | **Slow** | **Average** | **Strong** | **Unstoppable**

YAO ON
LEARNING FROM MISTAKES

SATURDAY	DATE

"It's like me studying English. I might learn a new word, and the second day I'll forget it and not use it. By the third day, I'll remember it again. In the process of learning, you're going to go through that. You're going to go through times when you make a mistake, and then you have to correct it again."

GOAL FOR THE DAY

RESISTANCE TRAINING

Muscle Group	Exercise	Warm-Up	Set 1	Set 2	Set 3	Cooldown	Comments

CARDIO ACTIVITY

Type of Exercise	Warm-Up Period	Sustained Heart Rate	Workout Period In Sustained Heart Rate	Cooldown Period

DIET

Day's Calories	Carbohydrates	Protein	Weight

SUCCESS/DISAPPOINTMENT OF THE DAY

Overall Grade: **A** | **B** | **C** | **D** | **F** How I felt today: **Exhausted** | **Slow** | **Average** | **Strong** | **Unstoppable**

YAO ON
SUCCESS

SUNDAY	DATE

"Everything will be based on my own hard work. Chinese people have a saying that to be successful there are two things you need. One is hard work, and the other is a little bit of luck."

GOAL FOR THE DAY

RESISTANCE TRAINING

Muscle Group	Exercise	Warm-Up	Set 1	Set 2	Set 3	Cooldown	Comments

CARDIO ACTIVITY

Type of Exercise	Warm-Up Period	Sustained Heart Rate	Workout Period In Sustained Heart Rate	Cooldown Period

DIET

Day's Calories	Carbohydrates	Protein	Weight

PERSEVERE

SUCCESS/DISAPPOINTMENT OF THE DAY

Overall Grade: **A** | **B** | **C** | **D** | **F**   How I felt today: **Exhausted** | **Slow** | **Average** | **Strong** | **Unstoppable**

WEEK 26 Inspiration: CRISTIANO RONALDO

Three-time FIFA Ballon d'Or World Player of the Year

MONDAY	DATE

VITAL STATS: Hometown: Madeira, Portugal
Born: February 5, 1985
Height: 6 ft 1 in / 185 cm Weight: 176 lb / 80 kg

GOAL FOR THE DAY

RESISTANCE TRAINING

Muscle Group	Exercise	Warm-Up	Set 1	Set 2	Set 3	Cooldown	Comments

CARDIO ACTIVITY

Type of Exercise	Warm-Up Period	Sustained Heart Rate	Workout Period In Sustained Heart Rate	Cooldown Period

DIET

Day's Calories	Carbohydrates	Protein	Weight

SUCCESS/DISAPPOINTMENT OF THE DAY

Overall Grade: **A** | **B** | **C** | **D** | **F**   How I felt today: **Exhausted** | **Slow** | **Average** | **Strong** | **Unstoppable**

CRISTIANO RONALDO is a free-flowing, fast, skillful, hugely athletic, goal-machine with a full locker of tricks, which he uses to bewilder opponents. He has played under the spotlight of arguably the two biggest clubs on the planet, Manchester United and Real Madrid, breaking goal-scoring records year after year, scoring more than a goal a game at Real. Ronaldo's personal battle with Barcelona's Argentinian striker, Lionel Messi, to be the world's best player, has seen him continually push the limits of his fitness, strength and talent.

TUESDAY | DATE

GOAL FOR THE DAY

RESISTANCE TRAINING

Muscle Group	Exercise	Warm-Up	Set 1	Set 2	Set 3	Cooldown	Comments

CARDIO ACTIVITY

Type of Exercise	Warm-Up Period	Sustained Heart Rate	Workout Period In Sustained Heart Rate	Cooldown Period

DIET

Day's Calories	Carbohydrates	Protein	Weight

SACRIFICE

SUCCESS/DISAPPOINTMENT OF THE DAY

Overall Grade: **A** | **B** | **C** | **D** | **F** How I felt today: **Exhausted** | **Slow** | **Average** | **Strong** | **Unstoppable**

RONALDO ON CONTINUOUS IMPROVEMENT

WEDNESDAY | DATE

"I am not a perfectionist, but I like to feel that things are done well. More important than that, I feel an endless need to learn, to improve, to evolve, not only to please the coach and the fans, but also to feel satisfied with myself. It is my conviction that there are no limits to learning, and that it can never stop, no matter what our age."

GOAL FOR THE DAY

RESISTANCE TRAINING

Muscle Group	Exercise	Warm-Up	Set 1	Set 2	Set 3	Cooldown	Comments

CARDIO ACTIVITY

Type of Exercise	Warm-Up Period	Sustained Heart Rate	Workout Period In Sustained Heart Rate	Cooldown Period

DIET

Day's Calories	Carbohydrates	Protein	Weight

SUCCESS/DISAPPOINTMENT OF THE DAY

Overall Grade: **A** | **B** | **C** | **D** | **F**   How I felt today: **Exhausted** | **Slow** | **Average** | **Strong** | **Unstoppable**

RONALDO ON
BEING THE BEST

THURSDAY | DATE

"I've never tried to hide the fact that it is my intention to become the best."

GOAL FOR THE DAY

RESISTANCE TRAINING

Muscle Group	Exercise	Warm-Up	Set 1	Set 2	Set 3	Cooldown	Comments

CARDIO ACTIVITY

Type of Exercise	Warm-Up Period	Sustained Heart Rate	Workout Period In Sustained Heart Rate	Cooldown Period

DIET

Day's Calories	Carbohydrates	Protein	Weight

SUCCESS/DISAPPOINTMENT OF THE DAY

BREAK THROUGH

Overall Grade: **A** | **B** | **C** | **D** | **F** How I felt today: **Exhausted** | **Slow** | **Average** | **Strong** | **Unstoppable**

RONALDO ON PERSONAL MOTIVATION

FRIDAY | DATE

"I know I'm a good professional, I know that no one's harder on me than myself and that's never going to change, under any circumstances."

GOAL FOR THE DAY

RESISTANCE TRAINING

Muscle Group	Exercise	Warm-Up	Set 1	Set 2	Set 3	Cooldown	Comments

CARDIO ACTIVITY

Type of Exercise	Warm-Up Period	Sustained Heart Rate	Workout Period In Sustained Heart Rate	Cooldown Period

DIET

Day's Calories	Carbohydrates	Protein	Weight

SUCCESS/DISAPPOINTMENT OF THE DAY

Overall Grade: **A** | **B** | **C** | **D** | **F** How I felt today: **Exhausted** | **Slow** | **Average** | **Strong** | **Unstoppable**

RONALDO ON
HUMBLENESS

SATURDAY	DATE

"When I win awards, I think of my father."

GOAL FOR THE DAY

RESISTANCE TRAINING

Muscle Group	Exercise	Warm-Up	Set 1	Set 2	Set 3	Cooldown	Comments

CARDIO ACTIVITY

Type of Exercise	Warm-Up Period	Sustained Heart Rate	Workout Period In Sustained Heart Rate	Cooldown Period

DIET

Day's Calories	Carbohydrates	Protein	Weight

WIN

SUCCESS/DISAPPOINTMENT OF THE DAY

Overall Grade: **A** | **B** | **C** | **D** | **F** How I felt today: **Exhausted** | **Slow** | **Average** | **Strong** | **Unstoppable**

RONALDO ON DREAMING

SUNDAY	DATE

"There is no harm in dreaming of becoming the world's best player. It's all about trying to be the best. I will keep working hard to achieve it, but it is within my capabilities."

GOAL FOR THE DAY

RESISTANCE TRAINING

Muscle Group	Exercise	Warm-Up	Set 1	Set 2	Set 3	Cooldown	Comments

CARDIO ACTIVITY

Type of Exercise	Warm-Up Period	Sustained Heart Rate	Workout Period In Sustained Heart Rate	Cooldown Period

DIET

Day's Calories	Carbohydrates	Protein	Weight

SUCCESS/DISAPPOINTMENT OF THE DAY

Overall Grade: **A** | **B** | **C** | **D** | **F** How I felt today: **Exhausted** | **Slow** | **Average** | **Strong** | **Unstoppable**

PERSONAL BREAKTHROUGHS

You broke through the wall! Whenever you achieve a noteworthy goal or a milestone worth remembering, record those breakthroughs here. When you feel you need a little extra encouragement and motivation, revisit these accomplishments and remind yourself what you're capable of. Fill these in whenever you accomplish something particularly inspiring.

WEEK-BY-WEEK WORKOUT TRACKER ACHIEVEMENT

Circle One: **Resistance Training** **Cardio Activity** **General Goals** DATE

Accomplishment:

What made this exceptional:

Feelings upon achieving this goal:

WEEK-BY-WEEK WORKOUT TRACKER ACHIEVEMENT

Circle One: **Resistance Training** **Cardio Activity** **General Goals** DATE

Accomplishment:

What made this exceptional:

Feelings upon achieving this goal:

WEEK-BY-WEEK WORKOUT TRACKER ACHIEVEMENT

Circle One: **Resistance Training** **Cardio Activity** **General Goals** DATE

Accomplishment:

What made this exceptional:

Feelings upon achieving this goal:

WEEK-BY-WEEK WORKOUT TRACKER ACHIEVEMENT

Circle One: **Resistance Training** **Cardio Activity** **General Goals** DATE

Accomplishment:

What made this exceptional:

Feelings upon achieving this goal:

WEEK-BY-WEEK WORKOUT TRACKER ACHIEVEMENT

Circle One: **Resistance Training** **Cardio Activity** **General Goals**

DATE

Accomplishment:

What made this exceptional:

Feelings upon achieving this goal:

WEEK-BY-WEEK WORKOUT TRACKER ACHIEVEMENT

Circle One: **Resistance Training** **Cardio Activity** **General Goals**

DATE

Accomplishment:

What made this exceptional:

Feelings upon achieving this goal:

WEEK-BY-WEEK WORKOUT TRACKER ACHIEVEMENT

Circle One: **Resistance Training** **Cardio Activity** **General Goals**

DATE

Accomplishment:

What made this exceptional:

Feelings upon achieving this goal:

WEEK-BY-WEEK WORKOUT TRACKER ACHIEVEMENT

Circle One: **Resistance Training** **Cardio Activity** **General Goals**

DATE

Accomplishment:

What made this exceptional:

Feelings upon achieving this goal:

WEEK-BY-WEEK WORKOUT TRACKER ACHIEVEMENT

Circle One: **Resistance Training** **Cardio Activity** **General Goals**

DATE

Accomplishment:

What made this exceptional:

Feelings upon achieving this goal:

WEEKLY JOURNAL

Use the spaces below to evaluate your progress at the end of each week of rigorous training. Try and focus on a lesson from each week—something you accomplished that surprised you, or a setback that you'll be wary of next time. The record will help you monitor your progress throughout the six-month program.

WEEK 1

WEEK 2

WEEK 3

WEEK 4

WEEK 5

WEEK 6

WEEK 7

WEEK 8

WEEK 9

WEEK 10

WEEK 11

WEEK 12

WEEKLY JOURNAL

WEEK 13

WEEK 14

WEEK 15

WEEK 16

WEEK 17

WEEK 18

WEEK 19

WEEK 20

WEEK 21

WEEK 22

WEEK 23

WEEK 24

WEEK 25

WEEK 26

MONITORING YOUR HEART RATE

Your **heart rate** is a reliable indicator of whether or not you're performing an exercise at an ideal intensity. As your workout increases in intensity, your muscles' demands for blood and oxygen increase, and your heart beats more rapidly in order to meet those demands.

Monitoring your heart rate during exercise is the best way to know whether the exercise's intensity is right for you. If you are serious about your workout and reaching your goals, there is a range of exercise intensities that can be both safe and effective in achieving the cardiovascular benefits you desire.

There are two things you have to look for:

Maximal Heart Rate is directly related to your age. As we age, our hearts beat more slowly. To calculate your Maximal Heart Rate, subtract your age from the number 220.

Target Heart Rate Range is the number of times per minute that your heart should beat during aerobic exercise. For most individuals, this range is 50 to 80 percent of your Maximal Heart Rate. Use the chart at the bottom of this page as a guide.

Once you've calculated your Target Heart Rate Range, use the numbers as a guideline in order to see how vigorously you should be working out. Immediately after finishing your workout, monitor your pulse rate by either checking your radial pulse at the base of the thumb of either hand or your carotid pulse at the side of your neck. Isolate the pulse by using the first two fingers of one hand to locate the artery. Count the number of beats in a ten-second period and multiply that by six in order to determine your beats per minute (bpm). That is your heart rate.

Remember that these are estimates, and if you feel like you are working too hard, you probably are. Reduce intensity, pace yourself and maintain a workout level that feels right for you.

CALCULATE YOUR HEART RATE ZONE BY AGE:

Age	20	30	40	50	60	70
Percentage of Maximal Heart Rate						
50%	100	95	90	85	80	75
80%	160	152	144	136	128	120

IDEAL BODY WEIGHTS

Reaching and maintaining your ideal body weight is an essential part of being the best athlete you can be. It is important you record your nutritional intake in your daily journal. As you work toward reaching, or maintaining, your ideal body weight, pay close attention to what you eat and how it affects your energy levels. Do you have the right balance of calories, proteins and carbohydrates to be satisfied and get through your workout?

Below are ideal weight charts for men and women based on the widely used tables originally produced by the Metropolitan Life Insurance Company. First you must determine your frame size.

You will need a tape measure to measure your wrist. Use that information to see whether you are small, medium, or large-boned in order to calculate your ideal body weight.

MEN	WOMEN
Small: wrist size under 6.5"/17 cm **Medium:** wrist size 6.5"/17 cm to 7.5"/19 cm **Large:** wrist size over 7.5"/19 cm	**Height: Under 5'2"/157 cm** **Small:** wrist size under 5.5"/14 cm **Medium:** wrist size 5.5"/17 cm to 5.75"/19 cm **Large:** wrist size over 5.75"/19 cm **Height: 5'2"/157 cm to 5'5"/165 cm** **Small:** wrist size under 6"/15 cm **Medium:** wrist size 6"/15 cm to 6.25"/16 cm **Large:** wrist size over 6.25"/16 cm **Height: Over 5'5"/165 cm** **Small:** wrist size under 6.25"/16 cm **Medium:** wrist size 6.25"/16 cm to 6.5"/17 cm **Large:** wrist size over 6.5"/17 cm

HEALTHY WEIGHTS IN POUNDS: MEN

Height	Small Frame	Medium Frame	Large Frame
5'2"	128–134	131–141	138–150
5'3"	130–136	133–143	140–153
5'4"	132–138	135–145	142–156
5'5"	134–140	137–148	144–160
5'6"	136–142	139–151	146–164
5'7"	138–145	142–154	149–168
5'8"	140–148	145–157	152–172
5'9"	142–151	148–160	155–176
5'10"	144–154	151–163	158–180
5'11"	146–157	154–166	161–184
6'0"	149–160	157–170	164–188
6'1"	152–164	160–174	168–192
6'2"	155–168	164–178	172–197
6'3"	158–172	167–182	176–202
6'4"	162–176	171–187	181–207

HEALTHY WEIGHTS IN POUNDS: WOMEN

Height	Small Frame	Medium Frame	Large Frame
4'10"	102–111	109–121	118–131
4'11"	103–113	111–123	120–134
5'0"	104–115	113–126	122–137
5'1"	106–118	115–129	125–140
5'2"	108–121	118–132	128–143
5'3"	111–124	121–135	131–147
5'4"	114–127	124–138	134–151
5'5"	117–130	127–141	137–155
5'6"	120–133	130–144	140–159
5'7"	123–136	133–147	143–163
5'8"	126–139	136–150	146–167
5'9"	129–142	139–153	149–170
5'10"	132–145	142–156	152–173
5'11"	135–148	145–159	155–176
6'0"	138–151	148–162	158–179

HEALTHY WEIGHTS IN KILOGRAMS: MEN

Height	Small Frame	Medium Frame	Large Frame
157 cm	58–61	59–64	63–68
160 cm	59–62	60–65	64–69
163 cm	60–63	61–66	64–71
165 cm	61–64	62–67	65–73
167 cm	62–64	63–68	66–74
170 cm	63–66	64–70	68–76
173 cm	64–67	66–71	69–78
175 cm	64–68	67–73	70–80
178 cm	65–70	68–74	72–82
180 cm	66–71	70–75	73–83
183 cm	68–73	71–77	74–85
185 cm	69–74	73–79	76–82
188 cm	70–76	74–81	78–89
191 cm	72–78	76–83	80–92
193 cm	73–80	78–85	82–94

HEALTHY WEIGHTS IN KILOGRAMS: WOMEN

Height	Small Frame	Medium Frame	Large Frame
147 cm	46–50	49–55	54–59
150 cm	47–51	50–56	54–63
152 cm	47–52	51–57	55–62
155 cm	48–54	52–59	57–64
157 cm	49–55	54–60	58–65
160 cm	50–56	55–61	59–67
163 cm	52–58	56–63	61–68
165 cm	53–59	57–64	62–70
167 cm	54–60	59–65	64–72
170 cm	56–62	60–67	65–74
173 cm	57–63	62–68	66–76
175 cm	59–64	63–69	68–77
178 cm	60–66	64–71	69–78
180 cm	61–67	66–72	70–80
183 cm	63–68	67–73	72–81

CREDITS

Athletes' quotes originally appear in the following:

pg. 14: Serena Williams. (n.d.). BrainyQuote.com. Retrieved July 29, 2015, from BrainyQuote.com Web site: http://www.brainyquote.com/quotes/quotes/s/serenawill183396.html
pg. 15: Serena Williams. (n.d.). BrainyQuote.com. Retrieved July 29, 2015, from BrainyQuote.com Web site: http://www.brainyquote.com/quotes/quotes/s/serenawill444249.html
pg. 16: Serena Williams. (n.d.). BrainyQuote.com. Retrieved July 29, 2015, from BrainyQuote.com Web site: http://www.brainyquote.com/quotes/quotes/s/serenawill444256.html
pg. 17: http://espn.go.com/tennis, Serena: 'No intention of stopping', June 23, 2012
pg. 18: Serena Williams. (n.d.). BrainyQuote.com. Retrieved July 29, 2015, from BrainyQuote.com Web site: http://www.brainyquote.com/quotes/quotes/s/serenawill183397.html
pg. 21: http://www.usolympicteam.com/10_questions/102402poli.html
pg. 22: http://www.stanford.edu/tempo?page=content&id=12075&repository=0001_article
pg. 23: *USA Today*, July 2, 2002.
pg. 24: *San Francisco Chronicle*, October 25, 2001, "Stanford's Azevedo a Natural, " John Crumpacker.
pg. 25: *Stanford Cardinal Chat Wrap*, October 11, 2001, http://www.fansonly.com/schools/stan/sports/m–wpolo/spec–rel/101101aab.html
pg. 28: *Sports Illustrated*, June 23, 2003, "Big Bend," Grant Wahl.
pg. 29: *Shoot Monthly*, May 2003, "Big with Becks."
pg. 30: *Manchester United Magazine*, June 2003, Issue 129.
pg. 31: *New York Times*, June 8, 2002.
pg. 32: *New York Times*, July 3, 2003.
pg. 35: *Texas Monthly*, August 2000, "Roger, Over and Out?" Michael P. Geffner.
pg. 36: *Texas Monthly*, August 2000, "Roger, Over and Out?" Michael P. Geffner.
pg. 37: http://www.baseball–almanac.com/quotes/roger_clemens_quotes.shtml
pg. 38: AP State & Local Wire, March 17, 2004, BC cycle.
pg. 39: *Milwaukee Journal Sentinel* (Wisconsin), October 11, 2003.
pg. 42: http://en.thinkexist.com/quotes/nadia–comaneci/
pg. 43: http://www.nadiacomaneci.com/index2.html
pg. 44: *Us Weekly*, March 26, 2001.
pg. 45: *The Hindu*, September 25, 2000, "Lion Queen Set to Bid Farewell."
pg. 46: *Seventeen*, November 1976, "What's Next for Nadia?" Frank Deford.
pg. 49: http://espn.go.com/classic/biography/s/DeLaHoya_Oscar.html
pg. 50: http://espn.go.com/classic/biography/s/DeLaHoya_Oscar.html
pg. 51: *Desert Sun* (Palm Springs, California), June 15, 2000, http://www.thedesertsun.com/news/stories/sports/961028163.shtml
pg. 52: *Sports Illustrated*, May 12, 2003.
pg. 53: *Sports Illustrated*, July 2, 2001.
pg. 56: *Guardian* (UK), April 8, 2002.
pg. 57: *Guardian* (UK), April 8, 2002.
pg. 58: *Sports Illustrated for Kids*, July 2000.
pg. 59: *New York Times*, February 25, 1998.
pg. 60: *New York Times*, February 25, 1998.
pg. 63: FIFATV, interview after the Women's World Cup Final, July 5, 2015

pg. 64: Speaking to the Associated Press after the Women's World Cup Final, July 5, 2015

pg. 65: http://theinscribermag.com/interviews-features-one-on-one-with-us-womens-soccer-player-carli-lloyd

pg. 66: Interview for USSoccer.com, Apr 29, 2015

pg. 67: http://www.thespectrum.com/story/sports/2015/07/06/captain-carli-greatest-minutes-ever/29800489/

pg. 70: Usain Bolt. (n.d.). BrainyQuote.com. Retrieved July 26, 2015, from BrainyQuote.com Web site: http://www.brainyquote.com/quotes/quotes/u/usainbolt447685.html

pg. 71: *Telegraph* (UK), May 23, 2012, Ian Chadband

pg. 72: Usain Bolt. (n.d.). BrainyQuote.com. Retrieved July 26, 2015, from BrainyQuote.com Web site: http://www.brainyquote.com/quotes/quotes/u/usainbolt447690.html

pg. 73: https://instagram.com/usainbolt/

pg. 74: Usain Bolt. (n.d.). BrainyQuote.com. Retrieved July 26, 2015, from BrainyQuote.com Web site: http://www.brainyquote.com/quotes/quotes/u/usainbolt447693.html

pg. 77: *Newsweek*, January 24, 1994.

pg. 78: *Newsweek*, January 5, 1987, Pete Axthelm.

pg. 79: Michael Jordan, at press conference announcing he was leaving the NBA to pursue a career in baseball.

pg. 80: *Jet*, October 15, 2001.

pg. 81: *ESPN.com* exclusive, Larry Schwartz.

pg. 84: *Jet*, October 19, 1998.

pg. 85: *Women's Sports & Fitness*, November/December 1998.

pg. 86: *Sports Illustrated*, August 3, 1998.

pg. 87: *Women's Sports & Fitness*, January/February 1995.

pg. 88: http://www.abouttimemag.com/aprart.html

pg. 91: http://en.wikipedia.org/wiki/Alexander_Karelin

pg. 92: http://karelin.ru/eng/?id=5

pg. 93: *Atlanta Journal and Constitution*, July 14, 1996.

pg. 94: http://espn.go.com/oly/summer00/wrestling/s/2000/0906/726828.html

pg. 95: http://espn.go.com/oly/summer00/wrestling/s/2000/0906/726828.html

pg. 98: *People*, January 15, 2001, "Iceman's Return," Alex Tresniowski, Cynthia Wang.

pg. 99: *New York Times*, October 26, 1992.

pg. 100: AP, September 29, 2003.

pg. 101: *Pittsburgh Post–Gazette* (Pennsylvania), August 30, 1994.

pg. 102: AP, September 27, 1995.

pg. 105: *Retirement announcement*, February 6, 2004, http://lennoxlewis.com

pg. 106: *Retirement announcement*, February 6, 2004, http://lennoxlewis.com

pg. 107: *Retirement announcement*, February 6, 2004, http://lennoxlewis.com

pg. 108: *Retirement announcement*, February 6, 2004, http://lennoxlewis.com

pg. 109: *Secondsout.com*, Thomas Hauser.

pg. 112: *Outside*, November 1998.

pg. 113: *Outside*, November 1998.

pg. 114: http://www.austria.org/oldsite/may98/herm.html

pg. 115: http://www.austria.org/oldsite/may98/herm.html

pg. 116: *World Ski News*, December 7, 2003, http://www.xtdev.com/ski/wmview_en.php?ArtID=315

pg. 119: https://www.facebook.com/sharapova

pg. 120: 2008 Australian Open victory speech

pg. 121: https://twitter.com/MariaSharapova

pg. 122: Maria Sharapova. (n.d.). BrainyQuote.com. Retrieved July 27, 2015, from BrainyQuote.com Web site: http://www.brainyquote.com/quotes/quotes/m/mariashara187573.html

pg. 123: 2006 Miami Open press conference

pg. 126: *Runner's World*, May 1994.

pg. 127: *Outside*, January 2004

pg. 128: *Women's Sports & Fitness*, March 1995.

pg. 129: *Rolling Stone*, April 21, 1994.

pg. 130: *Rolling Stone*, April 21, 1994.

pg. 133: *ESPN.com*, September 19, 2000.

pg. 134: *Netlondon.com*, September 15, 2000.

pg. 135: *Reuters*, September 3, 2000, Mitch Phillips.

pg. 136: *Daily Telegraph*

pg. 137: *Sunday London Times*, September 24, 2000

pg. 140: *Soul Surfer: A True Story of Faith, Family, and Fighting to Get Back on the Board*, Bethany Hamilton

pg. 141: *Soul Surfer: A True Story of Faith, Family, and Fighting to Get Back on the Board*, Bethany Hamilton

pg. 142: *Soul Surfer: A True Story of Faith, Family, and Fighting to Get Back on the Board*, Bethany Hamilton

pg. 143: *Soul Surfer: A True Story of Faith, Family, and Fighting to Get Back on the Board*, Bethany Hamilton

pg. 144: *Soul Surfer: A True Story of Faith, Family, and Fighting to Get Back on the Board*, Bethany Hamilton

pg. 147: http://www.famous–quotes–and–quotations.com/sports–quotes.html

pg. 148: http://216.239.39.104/search?q=cache:s2KFKagXlhgJ:www–pub.naz.edu:9000/~edauer5/quotes.htm+%22emmitt+smith%22+quotations&hl=en

pg. 149: *SI.com*, January 31, 1994.

pg. 150: *SI.com*, February 14, 1994.

pg. 151: *Houston Chronicle*, August 26, 2001.

pg. 154: http://www.iwf.net/publications/011/naim/html

pg. 155: *World Weightlifting Issue*: 2002

pg. 156: AP, September 17, 2000.

pg. 157: *Sports Illustrated*, October 3, 1988.

pg. 158: *Gazette* (Montreal), July 23, 1996.

pg. 161: http://ianthorpe.aol7.com.au/aboutian.php

pg. 162: *Newsweek*, September 18, 2000.

pg. 163: http://www.japantoday.com/gidx/news48481.html

pg. 164: *CNNSI.com*, September 14, 2000.

pg. 165: http://meganthorpe.topcities.com/tracey.html

pg. 168: LeBron James. (n.d.). BrainyQuote.com. Retrieved July 27, 2015, from BrainyQuote.com Web site: http://www.brainyquote.com/quotes/quotes/l/lebronjame425370.html

pg. 169: https://twitter.com/lebronjames/status/562994163596394498, Feb 4, 2015

pg. 170: LeBron James. (n.d.). BrainyQuote.com. Retrieved July 27, 2015, from BrainyQuote.com Web site: http://www.brainyquote.com/quotes/quotes/l/lebronjame425364.html

pg. 171: USA TODAY, "James' leadership skills loom large over the Cavaliers", David DuPree, November 21, 2005

pg. 172: LeBron James Interview, Chicago Pre-draft camp media conference, 2003

pg. 175: Gabby Douglas. (n.d.). BrainyQuote.com. Retrieved July 27, 2015, from BrainyQuote.com Web site: http://www.brainyquote.com/quotes/quotes/g/gabbydougl448191.html

pg. 176: http://www.goodreads.com/quotes/601424

pg. 177: Gabby Douglas. (n.d.). BrainyQuote.com. Retrieved July 27, 2015, from BrainyQuote.com Web site: http://www.brainyquote.com/quotes/quotes/g/gabbydougl448195.html

pg. 178: New York Daily News, August 23, 2012, Peter Botte

pg. 179: Interview with vibe.com, August 27, 2013

pg. 182: *Houston Chronicle*, February 22, 2004, Jonathan Feigen.

pg. 183: *Houston Chronicle*, January 26, 2004, Jonathan Feigen.

pg. 184: *Houston Chronicle*, December 24, 2003, Jonathan Feigen.

pg. 185: *Houston Chronicle*, December 8, 2003, Jonathan Feigen.

pg. 186: *Houston Chronicle*, Jonathan Feigen.

pg. 189: http://www.goodreads.com/quotes/155119

pg. 190: http://en.espn.co.uk/football/sport/story/258603.html

pg. 191: http://www.theguardian.com/football/2008/aug/07/manchesterunited.ronaldo1

pg. 192: http://www.ronaldo7.net/extra/quotes/cristiano-ronaldo-quotes.html

pg. 193: http://www.azquotes.com/quote/552126

Pages 21, 23, 25, 27, 93, 97, 127, 129, 133, 135, 137, 139, 161 and 179 courtesy Getty Images. Page 61 © Scott Anderson / Dreamstime; Page 63 © Luis Lopes Silva / Dreamstime; Page 65 © Leszek Wrona / Dreamstime; Pages 167, 169 and 171 © Dgareri / Dreamstime; Page 173 © Starstock / Dreamstime. Page 15 © Neale Cousland / Shutterstock; page 17 © Anatoliy Lukich / Shutterstock; page 19 © Leonard Zhukovsky / Shutterstock.com; Pages 67 and 119 © lev radin / Shutterstock; Page 69 © Ververidis Vasilis / Shutterstock ; Pages 71 and 73 © Kaliva / Shutterstock; Page 117 © 3777190317 / Shutterstock; Pages 121 and 123 © Neale Cousland / Shutterstock; Page 141 © jarvis gray / Shutterstock; Page 139 © Brian A. Witkin / Shutterstock; Page 143 © Alain Lauga / Shutterstock; Page 175 © JStone / Shutterstock; Page 177 © Ron Foster Sharif / Shutterstock; Pages 187 and 189 © AGIF / Shutterstock; and Pages 191 and 193 © Marcos Mesa Sam Wordley / Shutterstock.

All other photos courtesy of the Associated Press.

NOTES

NOTES

NOTES